THEORY
for
BEGINNERS

Barbara
Wharram

ISBN 0-88797-006-0

FREDERICK
HARRIS
MUSIC

BARBARA WHARRAM

MUS. BAC., A.R.C.T.

1928 — 1977

Born and raised in Toronto, Canada, Barbara Wharram graduated from Branksome Hall School; received her A.R.C.T., Solo Performer's piano, from the Royal Conservatory of Music, Toronto; and graduated from the Faculty of Music, University of Toronto.

After graduation Mrs. Wharram pursued her studies of all aspects of the theory of music with the late Eric Rollinson.

Mrs. Wharram is the author of the very popular theory book, ELEMENTARY RUDIMENTS OF MUSIC.

PREFACE

This book was written as a preliminary theory book designed to appeal to younger children, in answer to many requests from teachers using the ELEMENTARY RUDIMENTS OF MUSIC.

THEORY FOR BEGINNERS can be used by students of elementary school age as soon as they begin to study any musical instrument or undertake the formal study of music at school.

The illustrations, for which I am very grateful to one of my students, Robert Zalay, are drawn entirely from musical symbols. Games can be built around the sketches to help children learn these signs.

I wish to thank my younger private students and the children in the Junior Choir of St. Anne's Anglican Church, Toronto, whose reactions to my pilot program have guided me in finalizing this book. They have also served to strengthen my conviction that relating the written theory to ear training is an indispensible learning activity.

Barbara Wharram

1974

To my daughters Heather and Pam.

First Printing September, 1974
Thirty-Second Printing July, 1999

CONTENTS

CHAPTER 1.

THE KEYBOARD

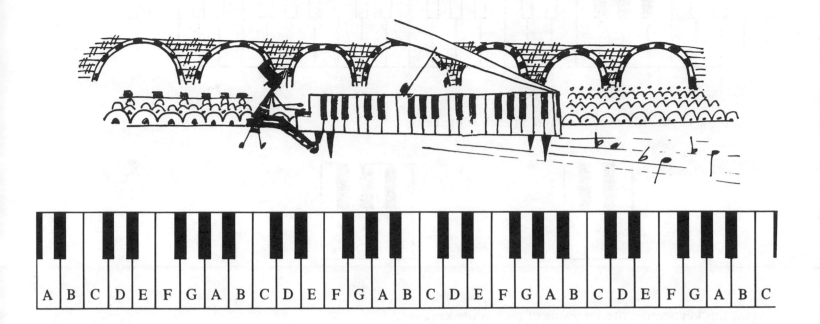

The piano keyboard has white keys and black keys.

The white keys have the same letter-names as the first seven letters of the alphabet — A B C D E F G. When we get to G we start all over again until we have named every key on the piano.

The black keys are arranged in groups of twos and threes.

Every key whose name is C is found just to the left of a group of two black keys.

The C nearest the middle of the piano is called Middle C.

EXERCISES

1. Darken all the groups of TWO black keys.

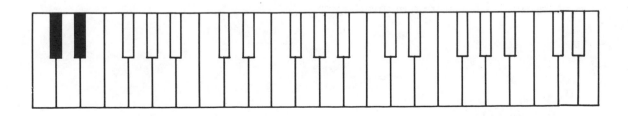

2. Darken all the groups of THREE black keys.

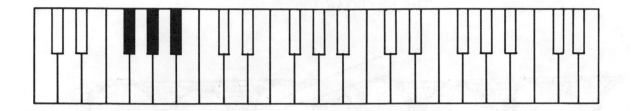

3. On these keyboards write the name of each white key.

4. On this keyboard write the name of each white key.

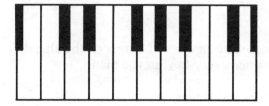

5. Fill in the blanks.

   a. The name of the note between the two black keys is _____

   b. The next white note down from A is _____

   c. The note that is just to the left of the three black keys is _____

   d. The next white note down from B is _____

   e. The note that is just to the right of the two black keys is _____

   f. The next note up from B is _____

   g. The note that is just to the right of the three black keys is _____

You will learn the names of the black keys later on in this chapter.

NOTE WRITING

Music is written on 5 lines and 4 spaces. This is called the STAFF.

These are the lines 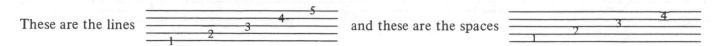 and these are the spaces

As you can see they are numbered from the bottom up.

We can put notes on any of these lines and spaces on the staff. The farther up a note is on the staff the higher its sound or PITCH will be. The farther down a note is on the staff the lower its pitch will be.

Notes are not perfectly round. They are oval. If you draw two curved lines like this ◐ and fit them together you will get the right shape. ⬭

A line note is written half above and half below the line. The line goes right through the middle of the note. ⊖

A space note is written exactly between two lines, touching them at the top and bottom. ⊠

EXERCISES

1. Draw 10 line notes. ⊖

2. Draw 10 space notes. ⊠

3. Write the number of the line that each of these notes is on.

   2

4. Write the number of the space that each of these notes is in.

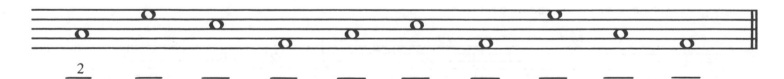

   2

5. Draw a circle around every line note.

4

6. Draw a circle around every space note.

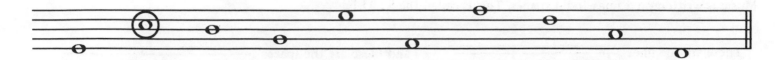

Notes often have short lines added to them called STEMS. Stems that point down are on the left side of the note: ♩
   Stems that point up are on the right side of the note: ♩

EXERCISES

1. Add stems to the left side.   o o o o o o o o o o

2. Add stems to the right side.   o o o o o o o o o o

3. Add stems going down.   o o o o o o o o o o

4. Add stems going up.   o o o o o o o o o o

5. Add stems correctly.

o o o o o o o o o o o o o

Up   Left   Right   Down   Right   Up   Down   Left   Down   Up   Right   Left

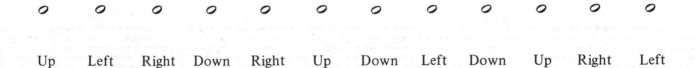

If the note is ON the middle line of the staff the stem may point either up or down.

If the note is ABOVE the middle line the stem usually goes down. If the note is BELOW the middle line the stem usually goes up. Look at these examples carefully.

EXERCISES

1. Add a stem to each of the following.

2. Draw notes with stems on the LINES shown by the numbers.

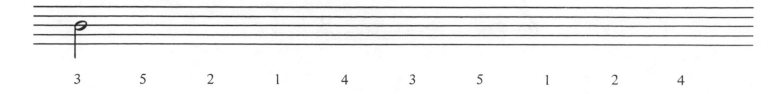

3   5   2   1   4   3   5   1   2   4

3. Draw notes with stems in the SPACES shown by the numbers.

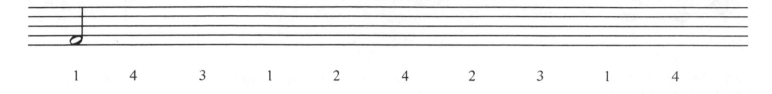

1   4   3   1   2   4   2   3   1   4

There can be a note on every line and in every space on the staff. Like the keys on the keyboard these notes are named in the same order as the first seven letters of the alphabet A B C D E F G.

A CLEF is a sign that is put at the beginning of every staff to show exactly where one particular note is.

This is the TREBLE or G CLEF. It curls around line 2 to show you where the G above middle C is.

To draw a treble clef follow these five steps.

1.   2.   3.   4.   5.

EXERCISE

Draw 10 treble clefs on each staff below.

You will remember that the treble clef tells us that G is on line 2, so the next space up is A, the next line up is B, the next space up is C, and so on.

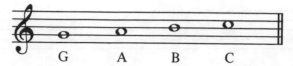

G   A   B   C

Here are all the notes in the treble clef.

C   D   E   F   G   A   B   C   D   E   F   G

Notice that the first C and D and also the last G are outside the staff, below and above. These new note positions are explained on page 16.   They are easier to remember if you learn the line notes and the space notes separately.

Here are the treble clef line notes

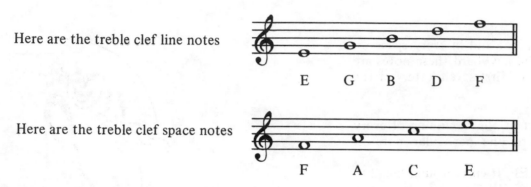

E   G   B   D   F

Here are the treble clef space notes

F   A   C   E

Perhaps a sentence using the names of the notes as the first letter for each word will help. The most popular one for the lines in the treble clef seems to be "Every Good Boy Deserves Fudge" but "Eat Good Bread Dear Father" works just as well. See if you can make up a sentence of your own.

Since F A C E spells a word and rhymes with S P A C E there is really no need for a sentence for the spaces in the treble clef.

EXERCISES

1. Draw a treble clef. Then draw a note on every line and name it.

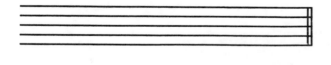

2. Draw a treble clef. Then draw a note in every space and name it.

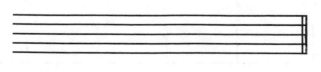

3. Add a stem to each of these line notes and name them.

_B_   ___   ___   ___   ___   ___   ___   ___

4. Add a stem to each of these space notes and name them.

___   ___   ___   ___   ___   ___   ___   ___   ___

5. Draw each of these as a line note with a stem.

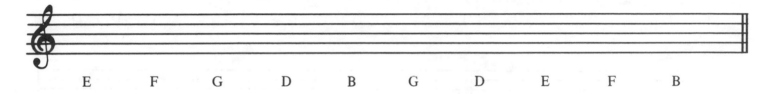

E   F   G   D   B   G   D   E   F   B

6. Draw each of these as a space note with a stem

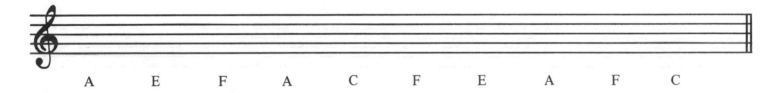

A   E   F   A   C   F   E   A   F   C

7. Add a treble clef at the beginning of each staff, and then name these notes.

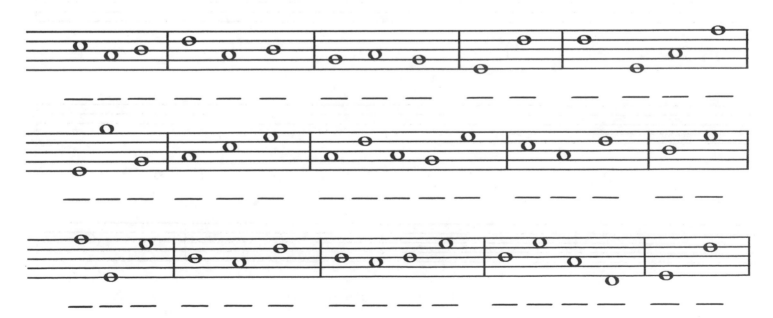

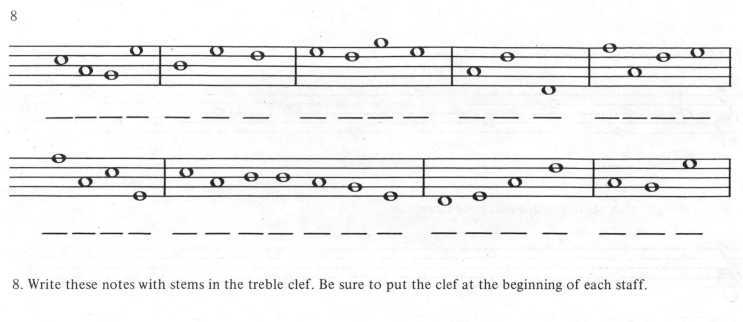

8. Write these notes with stems in the treble clef. Be sure to put the clef at the beginning of each staff.

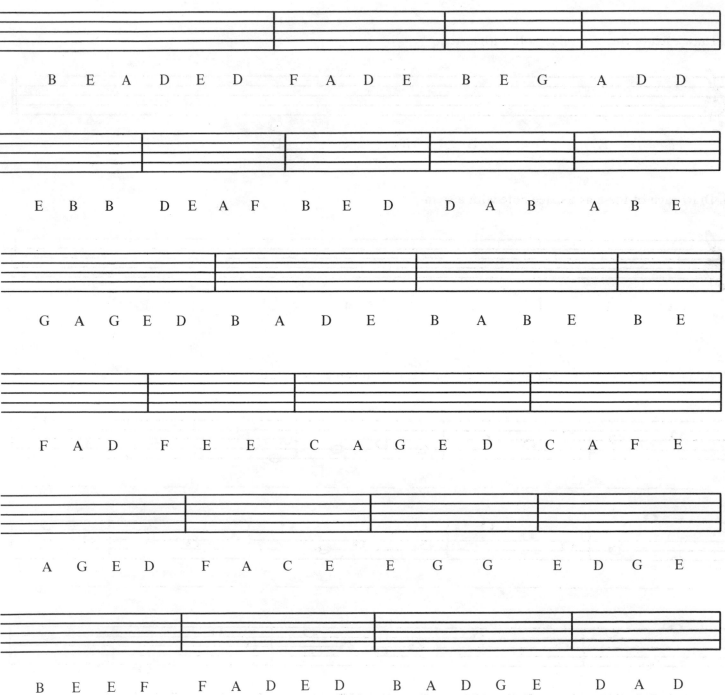

B E A D E D   F A D E   B E G   A D D

E B B   D E A F   B E D   D A B   A B E

G A G E D   B A D E   B A B E   B E

F A D   F E E   C A G E D   C A F E

A G E D   F A C E   E G G   E D G E

B E E F   F A D E D   B A D G E   D A D

ACROSS

1.

2.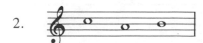

5.

6.

8.

11.

14.

15.

16.

17.

DOWN

1.

2.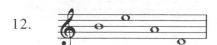

3.

4.

7.

9.

10.

12.

13.

This is the BASS or F CLEF. The two dots in the third and fourth spaces show you where the F below middle C is.

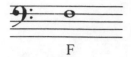

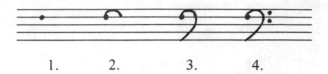

F

To draw a bass clef start with a dot on line 4, curve up to the top line, around and down to the bottom space. Then add the two very important dots in spaces 3 and 4.

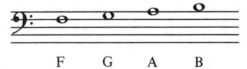

1.   2.   3.   4.

EXERCISE

Draw 10 bass clefs on each staff below.

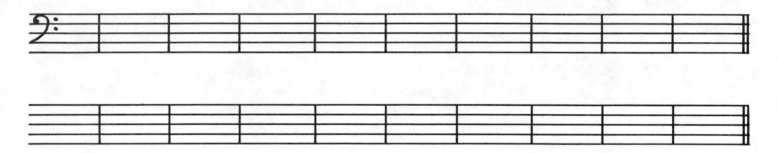

Since you know that F is on line 4, then if you follow the letters of the alphabet you will find that the next space up is G, the next line up is A and so on.

F   G   A   B

Here are all the notes in the bass clef.

F G A B C D E F G A B C

Notice that the first note (F) and the last two (B and C) are outside the staff. These new notes are explained on page 17.

Learn the lines and spaces separately as you did in the treble clef.

Here are the bass clef line notes.

Here are the bass clef space notes.

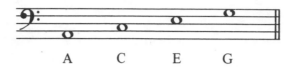

A good sentence for the bass clef line notes is "Good Boys Deserve Fudge Always" or "George Brown Does Feel Awful" or "Gertrude Buys Dark Fresh Apples" or an even better one that you make up yourself. For the spaces try "All Cows Eat Grass" or do you prefer "Are Cats Ever Green"?

EXERCISES

1. Draw a bass clef. Then draw a note on every line and name it.

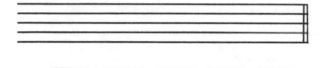

2. Draw a bass clef. Then draw a note in every space and name it.

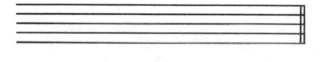

3. Add a stem to each of these line notes and name them.

4. Add a stem to each of these space notes and name them.

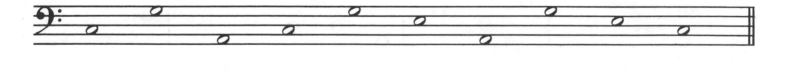

5. Draw each of these as a line note with a stem.

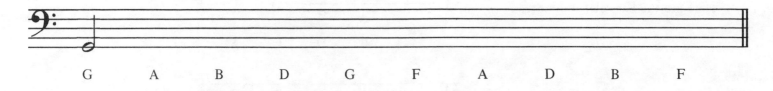

    G   A   B   D   G   F   A   D   B   F

6. Draw each of these as a space note with a stem.

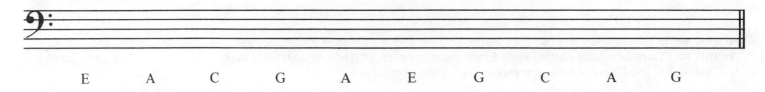

    E   A   C   G   A   E   G   C   A   G

7. Add a bass clef at the beginning of each staff and then name the notes.

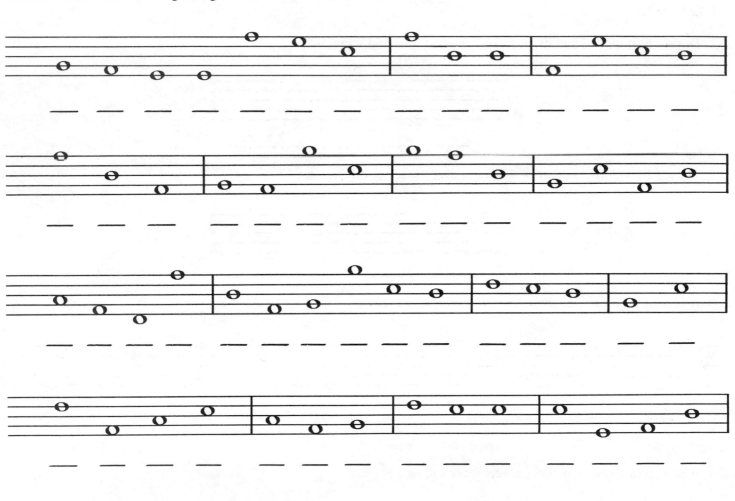

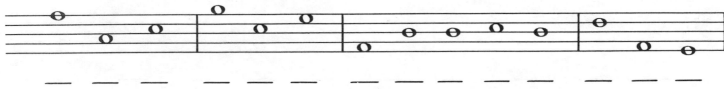

8. Write these notes with stems, in the bass clef. Remember to put the clef at the beginning of each staff.

G A G   B A D   F A D E D   G A F F

A G E D   A C E   B A D E   E G G   B E

D E A F   C A G E D   F E E D   G A G E

E D G E   D E F A C E   C A B   B E A D

9. Name these notes.

10. Decide whether these notes must have a treble clef or a bass clef, and draw it at the beginning of each bar.

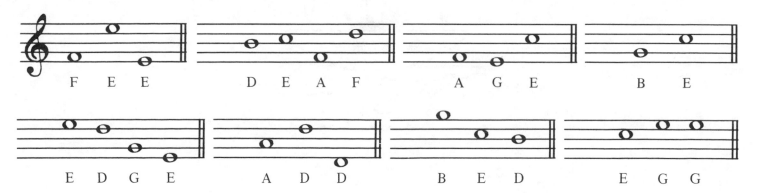

F E E   D E A F   A G E   B E

E D G E   A D D   B E D   E G G

11. Write each of these notes with a stem, in BOTH clefs. Remember to draw the clefs first.

F A D E D   C A B B A G E   B E G

B E E F   B A A   D E E D   B E A D

D A B B E D   B A D G E   F A C E D

𝄢

	1		2		3			4
5								
6					7			
		8		9				
				10			11	
		12	13					
			14		15			
16					17			

ACROSS

3.

5.

6.

7.

8.

10.

11.

12.

14.

16.

17.

DOWN

1.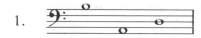

2.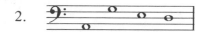

4.

5.

7.

8.

9.

13.

15.

The GRAND STAFF is used for piano music. It is made up of a staff with a treble clef and a staff with a bass clef joined together by a BAR LINE and a BRACKET or BRACE.

bracket ← → bar line

How to draw a bracket:

1.   2.   3.

The space between the two staves is where you put Middle C.

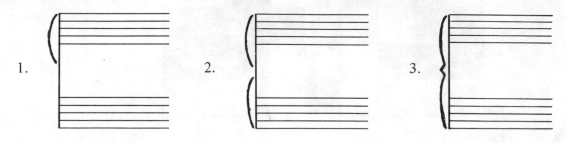

Middle C in the treble clef
(played with the right hand)

Middle C in the bass clef
(played with the left hand)

EXERCISE

Make each of these into a Grand Staff by adding a bar line, a bracket and the two clefs. Write Middle C for each hand.

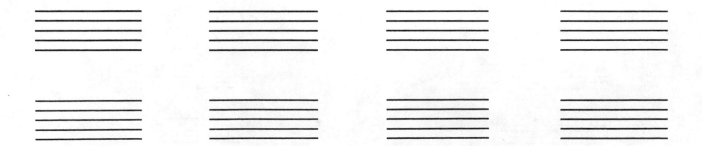

LEGER LINES are small lines used for writing notes that will not fit on the staff because they are too high or too low.

Middle C is written on the first leger line below the treble clef, and on the first leger line above the bass clef.

You know that this is G.  The next note up (A) will not fit on the staff so you must draw a line for it to go on. The B will sit on the first leger line, and C will need a second leger line.

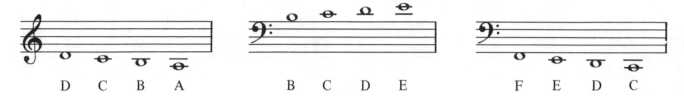

Follow the same steps to put notes on the leger lines below the treble clef, and above and below the bass clef.

Notice that the note on the second leger line above the treble clef and the note on the second leger line below the bass clef are both C's.

Make sure that you draw the leger lines the SAME distance apart as the lines of the staff.

Right   Wrong

EXERCISES

1. Name these notes.

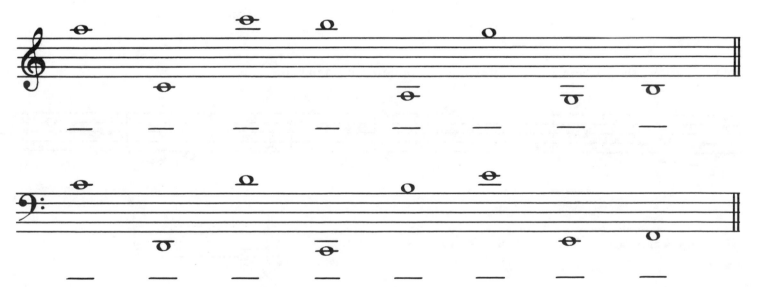

2. Write these notes using leger lines ABOVE the staff.

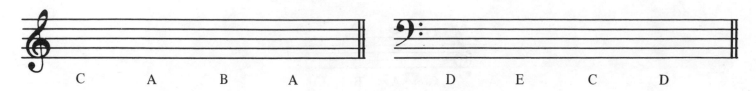

C   A   B   A   D   E   C   D

3. Write these notes using leger lines BELOW the staff.

A   C   B   A   E   C   D   E

Music is much easier to read when you know the direction in which the notes are moving: upwards, downwards or even standing still.

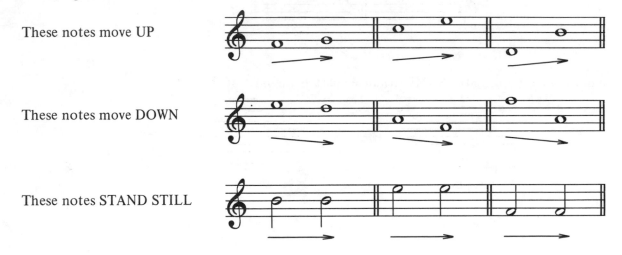

These notes move UP

These notes move DOWN

These notes STAND STILL

EXERCISE

By using arrows show whether these notes move up or down or stand still.

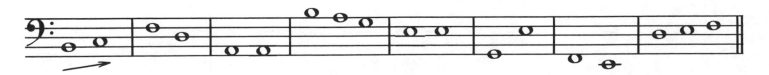

These notes move UP by STEP — from a line to a space to a line.

These notes move DOWN by STEP — from a line to a space to a line.

EXERCISES

1. Write two notes that move up by step from each of these notes.

2. Write two notes that move down by step from each of these notes.

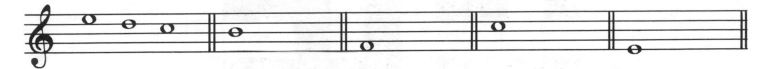

These notes move UP by SKIP from one space to the next space (skipping the line between) or from one line to the next line (skipping the space between.)

These notes move DOWN by SKIP from one space to the next space or from one line to the next line.

These are called skips of a third because we skip from the first note to the third note up or down.

Of course notes can move by bigger skips. You will learn more about these later.

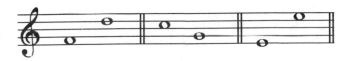

EXERCISES

1. Write two more notes that move up by skips of a third from each of these notes.

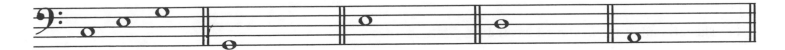

2. Write two more notes that move down by skips of a third from each of these notes.

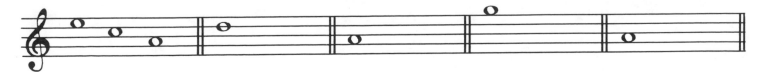

THE PIANO

ACROSS

1. What your fingers play on the piano.

5. This hits the string.

6. Keys are usually made of _____ .

8. 'Una corda' means to use the soft _____ .

10. This is a group of black keys.

11. The left end of the keyboard has the _____ notes.

12. Play to the bottom of the _____ .

DOWN

2. This vibrates to make the sound.

3. Keys are either black or _____ .

4. The whole set of keys.

7. C♯ and G♭ are _____ keys.

9. The pedals are pushed _____ .

SEMITONES AND ACCIDENTALS.

A SEMITONE is the distance from one key to the very next key (either up or down) with no key between.

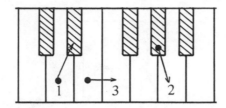

Look at the above keyboard and you will see that a semitone can be
1. from any white key to the black one next to it
2. from any black key to the white one next to it
3. from any white key to the next white key if there is no black key between them (that is between E and F, and between B and C.)

EXERCISE

Draw arrows to show semitones
- from a white key to a black key
- from a black key to a white key
- from a white key to a white key.

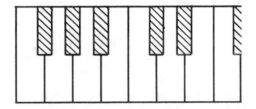

An ACCIDENTAL is a sign that is put BEFORE a note to change its pitch by making it higher or lower. It is always drawn on exactly the same line or space as the note that is being changed.

This is a SHARP. ♯ Drawing a sharp in front of a note RAISES it a semitone.

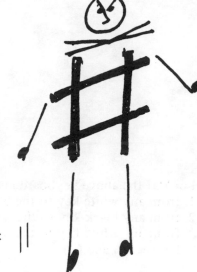

Notice that we *say* "C sharp" but it is written "sharp C".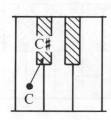

This is how to draw a sharp.

    1. Draw two straight lines down with the second one a little higher than the first: ||

    2. Cross them with two slanted lines like this: ♯

EXERCISES

1. Draw ten sharps on the second line of this staff.

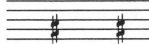

2. Draw ten sharps in the third space of this staff.

3. Draw a sharp in front of each of these notes remembering to put it on exactly the same line or space as the note. Then name each note.

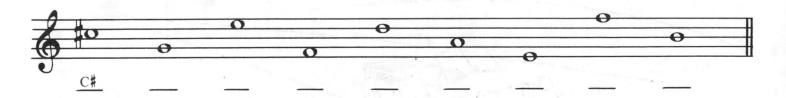

    C♯

This is a FLAT. ♭ Drawing a flat in front of a note LOWERS it a semitone.

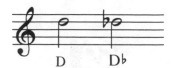

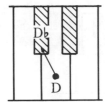

This is how to draw a flat.

1. Draw a straight line down: |

2. Draw half a heart at the bottom of it, on the right side: ♭

EXERCISES

1. Draw ten flats on the third line of this staff.

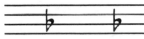

2. Draw ten flats in the second space of this staff.

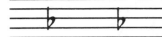

3. Draw a flat in front of each of these notes, putting it on exactly the same line or space as the note. Then name each note.

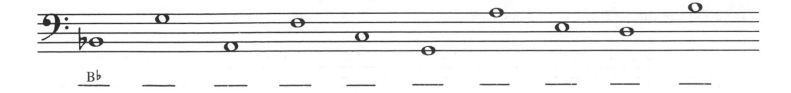

B♭ ___ ___ ___ ___ ___ ___ ___ ___ ___

This is a NATURAL. ♮ Drawing a natural in front of a note cancels a sharp or a flat. If the natural comes after a sharp it lowers a note.

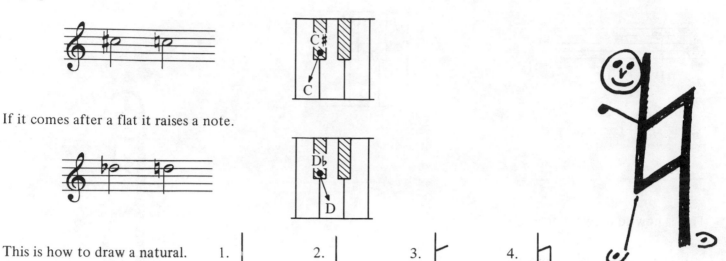

If it comes after a flat it raises a note.

This is how to draw a natural.   1.   2.   3.   4.   ♮

Any accidental affects all the notes after it on the SAME line or space for one full measure or until it is cancelled by another accidental.

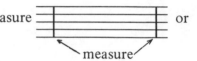

measure

G   G♭   G♭   G♮

Notice in the example below that the sharp does not affect the high F.

F♯   F   F♯

EXERCISES

1. Draw ten naturals on the fourth line of this staff.

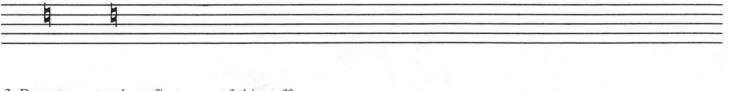

2. Draw ten naturals on first space of this staff.

25

3. Draw an arrow to show whether the second note is higher or lower than the first.

4. Draw a natural in front of each of these notes.

5. Name these notes.

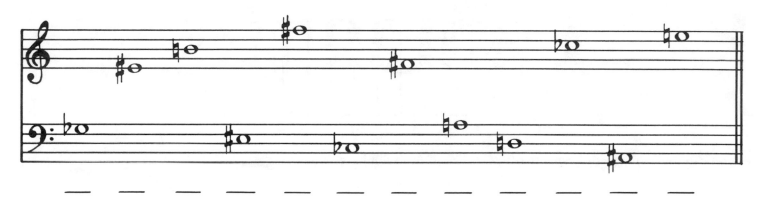

6. Write these notes in the treble clef. Use naturals where necessary.

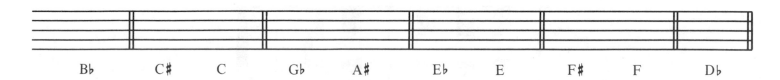

Bb   C#   C   Gb   A#   Eb   E   F#   F   Db

7. Write these notes in the bass clef.

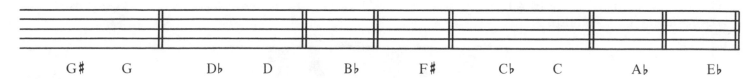

G#   G   Db   D   Bb   F#   Cb   C   Ab   Eb

26

On the keyboard sharp keys are one semitone to the right (since they are raised) and flat keys are one semitone to the left (since they are lowered.)

The black keys do not have names of their own and they have to borrow from one of the white keys nearest them. If the black key between C and D borrows from C it is C raised and is called C sharp; but if it borrows from D it is D lowered and is called D flat. So each black key may be called by two different names.

Most of the time a sharp key is a black one — for example F♯ and C♯. But remember that a sharp can raise ANY note without changing its letter-name, so when you raise E a semitone it will be E sharp, and when you raise B a semitone it will be B sharp — and both of these notes are WHITE. These are the only two white sharp keys.

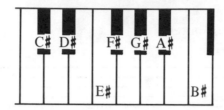

Similarly, a flat key is usually a black one, such as Bb or Eb, but when C and F are lowered a semitone you find that Cb and Fb are WHITE.

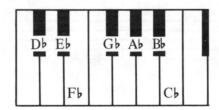

You can see from the diagrams that B, C, E and F can each have two names.

EXERCISES

1. On the keyboard write the SHARP letter-name of each black key. There are also two white keys that can have a sharp name. Write these also.

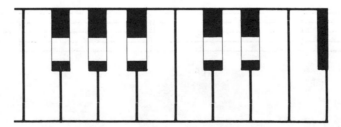

2. On the keyboard write the FLAT letter-name of each black key. There are also two white keys that can have a flat name. Write these also.

3. Give another name for each of these notes.

Ab _____ F# _____ B _____ Eb _____ E# _____ D# _____ Gb _____ C _____

A CHROMATIC SEMITONE is made up of two notes or keys with the SAME letter-name.

Examples: C♯ is a chromatic semitone ABOVE C

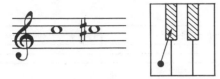

E♮ is a chromatic semitone ABOVE E♭

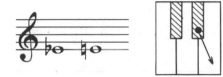

G♭ is a chromatic semitone BELOW G

A♮ is a chromatic semitone BELOW A♯

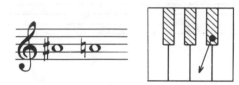

EXERCISES

1. Write a chromatic semitone ABOVE each of these notes.

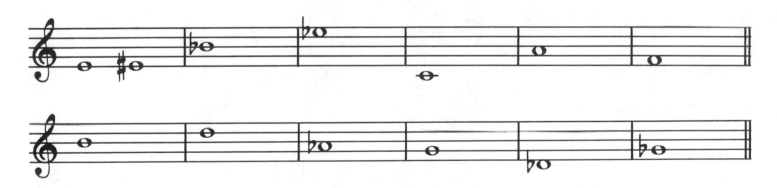

2. Write a chromatic semitone BELOW each of these notes.

3. Write a chromatic semitone ABOVE each of these notes.

4. Write a chromatic semitone BELOW each of these notes.

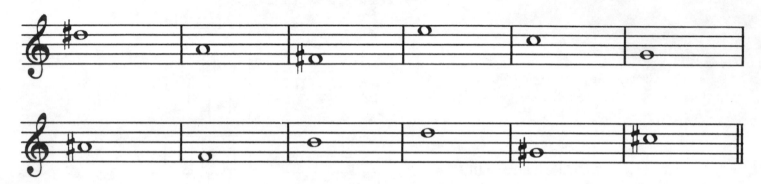

A DIATONIC SEMITONE is made up of two notes or keys with DIFFERENT letter-names.

Examples:

Db is a diatonic semitone ABOVE C

E is a diatonic semitone ABOVE D♯

F♯ is a diatonic semitone BELOW G

A is a diatonic semitone BELOW Bb

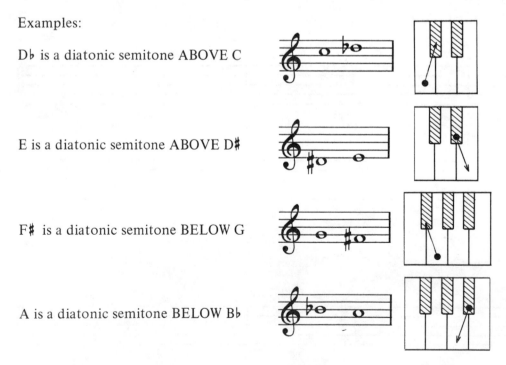

REMEMBER: Both Diatonic and Different start with a D!

EXERCISES

1. Write a diatonic semitone ABOVE each of these notes.

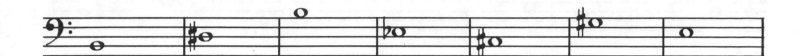

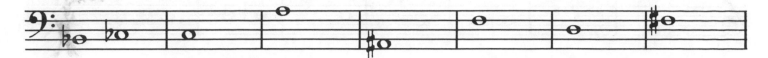

2. Write a diatonic semitone BELOW each of these notes.

3. Write a diatonic semitone ABOVE each of these notes.

4. Write a diatonic semitone BELOW each of these notes.

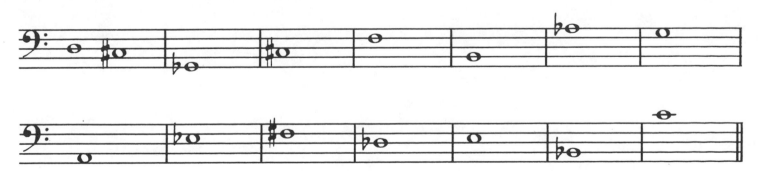

30

5. These are either chromatic semitones or diatonic semitones. If they are chromatic, write c.s.; if they are diatonic write d.s.

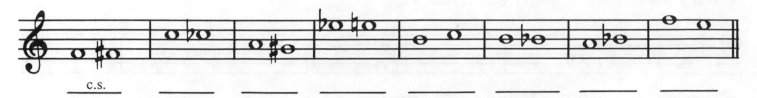

c.s.

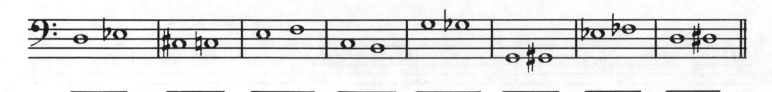

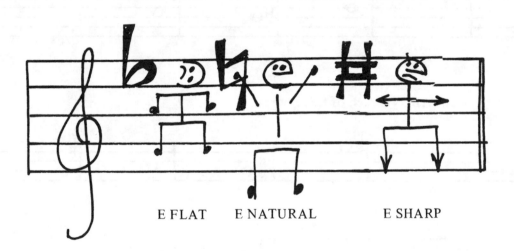

E FLAT   E NATURAL   E SHARP

WHOLE TONES.

A WHOLE TONE is made up of two semitones that are next to each other. There will always be one key (either black or white) between the notes of a whole tone.

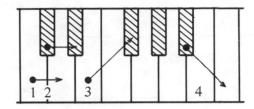

Look at the above keyboard and you will see that a whole tone can be

1. from a white key to the next white key if there is a black key between.
2. from a black key to the next black key if there is one white key between.
3. from a white key to the next black key if there is a white key between.
4. from a black key to a white key if there is a white key between.

More Examples:

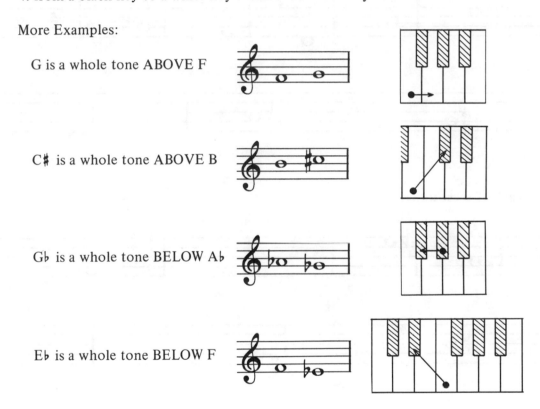

G is a whole tone ABOVE F

C♯ is a whole tone ABOVE B

G♭ is a whole tone BELOW A♭

E♭ is a whole tone BELOW F

EXERCISES

1. Draw arrows to mark all the whole tones on this keyboard. If you mark them all you will have found eleven.

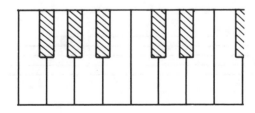

2. a. Name the whole tones UP from C to G♯ .

          <u>C</u>   <u>   </u>   <u>   </u>   <u>   </u>   <u>   </u>

   b. Name the whole tones UP from D♭ to A.

          <u>D♭</u>   <u>   </u>   <u>   </u>   <u>   </u>   <u>   </u>

   c. Name the whole tones DOWN from E to A♭ .

          <u>E</u>   <u>   </u>   <u>   </u>   <u>   </u>   <u>   </u>

   d. Name the whole tones DOWN from C♯ to F.

          <u>C♯</u>   <u>   </u>   <u>   </u>   <u>   </u>   <u>   </u>

3. Write a whole tone ABOVE each of these notes.

4. Write a whole tone BELOW each of these notes.

5. Write a whole tone BELOW each of these notes.

6. Write a whole tone ABOVE each of these notes.

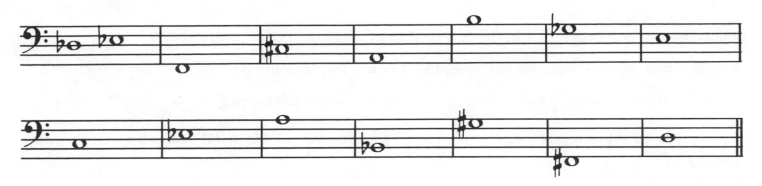

7. Is each of the following a whole tone (w.t.), a chromatic semitone (c.s.), or a diatonic semitone (d.s.)?

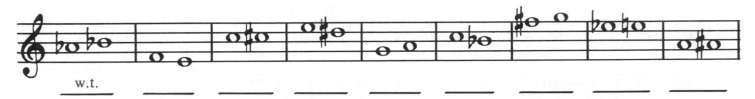

w.t. _____ _____ _____ _____ _____ _____ _____ _____

_____ _____ _____ _____ _____ _____ _____ _____

8. By adding accidentals make each of these pairs of notes a whole tone apart.

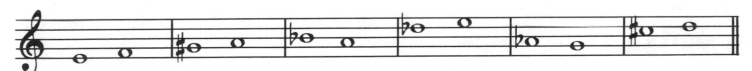

9. By adding accidentals make each of these pairs of notes a semitone apart.

10. Fill in the blanks by writing either 'whole tone' or 'semitone'.

a) B to C♯ is a _____

b) D♭ to D is a _____

c) F to G is a _____

d) G♯ to A♯ is a _____

e) A♭ to B♭ is a _____

f) E to F is a _____

g) G to F♯ is a _____

h) D to E is a _____

i) F♯ to E is a _____

j) B♭ to B is a _____

TIME VALUES.

Sounds in music have different LENGTHS or DURATIONS as well as different pitches.

In writing music different kinds of notes are used to show how long the sound is to last.

A WHOLE NOTE is used for the longest sound. This is a white note which has no stem. 𝅝

If you want a sound to last only half as long as a whole note you use a HALF NOTE. This is a white note with a stem.

If you want a sound to last only half as long as the half note you use a QUARTER NOTE. This is a black note with a stem.

If you want a short sound lasting only half as long as a quarter note you use an EIGHTH NOTE. This is a black note with a stem and a flag. Notice that the flag always curves to the right whether the stem is up or down.

Sometimes eighth notes are written in groups, with their stems joined by a line which is called a BEAM.

The shortest note that you will probably use at the present time is only half as long as the eighth note. It is called a SIXTEENTH NOTE. It is a black note with a stem and two flags. Sixteenth notes also come in groups with their stems joined by two beams.

EXERCISES

1. Write a whole note on each line and space.

2. Write 10 half notes on line 5.

3. Write 10 half notes on line 2.

4. Write 10 quarter notes in space 4.

5. Write 10 quarter notes in space 1.

6. Write 10 separate eighth notes on line 4.

7. Write 10 separate eighth notes on line 1.

8. Write 6 pairs of eighth notes on line 3. (Join each pair with a beam.)

9. Write 6 pairs of eighth notes in space 1.

10. Write 10 separate sixteenth notes on line 5.

11. Write 10 separate sixteenth notes in space 1.

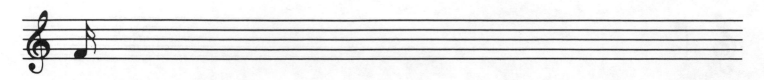

12. Write 4 groups of 4 sixteenth notes on line 2.

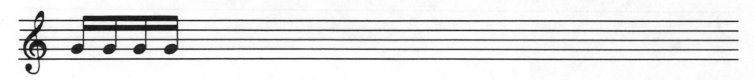

13. Write 4 groups of 4 sixteenth notes in space 4.

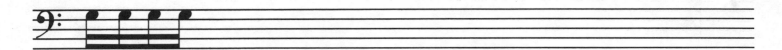

RESTS are signs which show periods of silence. There is a rest that has the same value as each kind of note.

whole note	𝅝	▬	whole rest
half note	𝅗𝅥	▬	half rest
quarter note	𝅘𝅥	𝄽	quarter rest
eighth note	𝅘𝅥𝅮	𝄾	eighth rest
sixteenth note	𝅘𝅥𝅯	𝄿	sixteenth rest

Be sure that you know where the whole rest and the half rest go. They are both in space 3 but the whole rest HANGS DOWN from line 4 and the half rest SITS ON line 3.

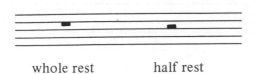

whole rest   half rest

The quarter rest can be easily drawn if you follow these 4 steps:

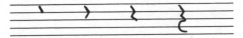

The eighth rest can be drawn in these 3 steps:

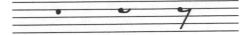

The sixteenth rest just has another flag added to the eighth rest.

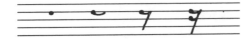

Always start to draw these rests in space three.

EXERCISES

1. Draw 10 quarter rests.

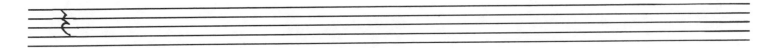

2. Draw 10 eighth rests.

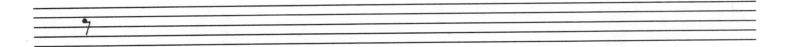

3. Draw 10 whole rests.

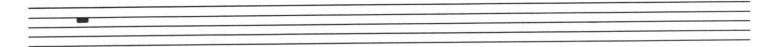

4. Draw 10 half rests.

5. Draw 10 sixteenth rests.

38

6. Write and name the kind of rest that has the same value as each of these notes.

♪ = 𝄾   eighth rest

𝅝 =

♪ =

♩ =

𝅘𝅥𝅯 =

𝅗𝅥 =

7. Write and name the kind of note that has the same value as each of these rests.

𝄽 = ♩   quarter note

𝄾 =

𝄾 =

𝄻 =

𝄽 =

𝄼 =

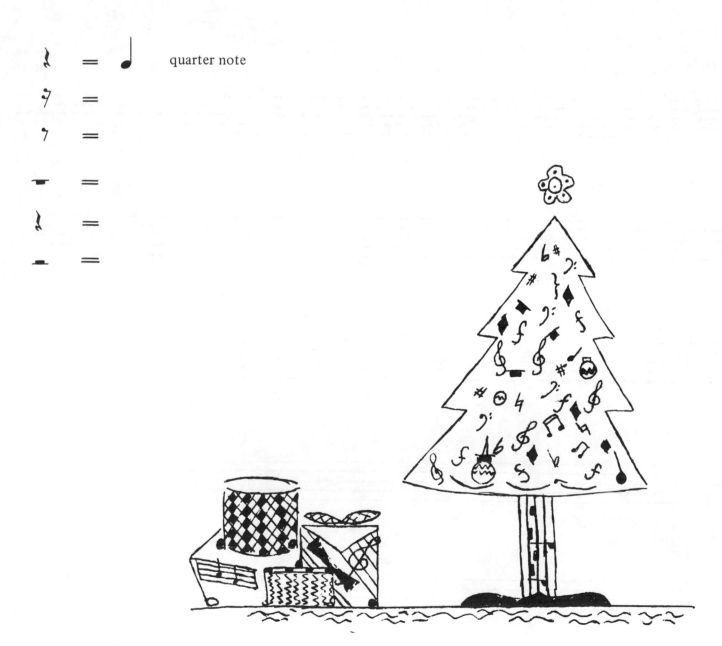

THE RELATIVE VALUE OF NOTES OR RESTS.

When the minute hand of a clock makes one complete circle a WHOLE hour has passed.

When the minute hand moves from 12 to 6 a HALF hour has passed. There are 2 HALF hours in one WHOLE hour.

When the minute hand moves from 12 to 3 a QUARTER hour has passed. There are 2 QUARTER hours in a HALF hour, and 4 QUARTER hours in a WHOLE hour.

It is the same with the time value of notes and rests.

A WHOLE NOTE can be divided into

2 HALF NOTES, and each half note can be divided into

2 QUARTER NOTES. 4 quarter notes equal 1 whole note.

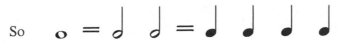

Similarly,

A WHOLE REST can be divided into

2 HALF RESTS, and each half rest can be divided into

2 QUARTER RESTS. 4 quarter rests equal 1 whole rest.

40

EXERCISES

1. Write ONE note that has the same total value as:

   a. ♩ + ♩ =

   b. ♩ + ♩ + ♩ =

   c. ♩ + ♩ =

   d. ♩ + ♩ + ♩ =

   e. ♩ + ♩ + ♩ + ♩ =

2. Write TWO notes that have the same total value as:

   a. 𝅝 =

   b. 𝅗𝅥 =

   c. ♩ + ♩ + ♩ + ♩ =

3. Fill in the blanks.

   a. 1 𝅝 = _____2_____ 𝅗𝅥

   b. 2 ♩ = _____ 𝅗𝅥

   c. 1 𝅝 = _____ ♩

   d. 2 𝅗𝅥 = _____ 𝅝

   e. 2 𝅝 = _____ 𝅗𝅥

   f. 2 𝅗𝅥 = _____ ♩

   g. 1 𝅗𝅥 = _____ ♩

   h. 4 ♩ = _____ 𝅗𝅥

   i. 4 ♩ = _____ 𝅝

   j. 4 𝅗𝅥 = _____ 𝅝

4. Fill in the blanks.

   a. 4 ▬ = _____ ▬

   b. 4 𝄽 = _____ ▬

   c. 4 𝄽 = _____ ▬

   d. 1 ▬ = _____ 𝄾

   e. 2 ▬ = _____ 𝄾

f. 2 𝄼 = _____ 𝄻

g. 2 𝄻 = _____ 𝄼

h. 1 𝄼 = _____ 𝄽

i. 2 𝄽 = _____ 𝄻

j. 1 𝄼 = _____ 𝄻

5. What is the sum in WHOLE NOTES of each of these?

a. 𝅗𝅥 𝅘𝅥 𝅘𝅥 = _____1_____ 𝅝

b. 𝅗𝅥 𝅗𝅥 𝅘𝅥 𝅘𝅥 𝅗𝅥 = _____ 𝅝

c. 𝅘𝅥 𝅘𝅥 𝅘𝅥 𝅘𝅥 𝅝 𝅗𝅥 𝅗𝅥 = _____ 𝅝

d. 𝅝 𝅗𝅥 𝅘𝅥 𝅘𝅥 𝅝 𝅘𝅥 𝅘𝅥 𝅘𝅥 = _____ 𝅝

e. 𝅘𝅥 𝅘𝅥 𝅘𝅥 𝅗𝅥 𝅗𝅥 𝅝 = _____ 𝅝

f. 𝅝 𝅗𝅥 𝅗𝅥 𝅝 𝅘𝅥 𝅘𝅥 𝅘𝅥 𝅘𝅥 𝅗𝅥 = _____ 𝅝

g. 𝅗𝅥 𝅗𝅥 𝅘𝅥 𝅘𝅥 𝅘𝅥 𝅘𝅥 𝅝 𝅗𝅥 𝅗𝅥 = _____ 𝅝

h. 𝅝 𝅘𝅥 𝅘𝅥 𝅗𝅥 𝅝 = _____ 𝅝

i. 𝅗𝅥 𝅘𝅥 𝅘𝅥 𝅘𝅥 𝅘𝅥 𝅘𝅥 𝅘𝅥 = _____ 𝅝

j. 𝅗𝅥 𝅘𝅥 𝅘𝅥 𝅝 𝅝 𝅘𝅥 𝅘𝅥 𝅝 = _____ 𝅝

6. What is the sum in HALF NOTES of each of these?

a. 𝅘𝅥 𝅘𝅥 𝅗𝅥 𝅗𝅥 = _____3_____ 𝅗𝅥

b. 𝅗𝅥 𝅝 𝅗𝅥 = _____ 𝅗𝅥

c. 𝅗𝅥 𝅘𝅥 𝅘𝅥 𝅘𝅥 𝅘𝅥 𝅘𝅥 𝅗𝅥 = _____ 𝅗𝅥

d. 𝅝 𝅘𝅥 𝅘𝅥 𝅗𝅥 = _____ 𝅗𝅥

e. 𝅗𝅥 𝅗𝅥 𝅝 𝅘𝅥 𝅘𝅥 𝅘𝅥 𝅘𝅥 = _____ 𝅗𝅥

f. 𝅘𝅥 𝅘𝅥 𝅗𝅥 𝅝 𝅗𝅥 𝅝 = _____ 𝅗𝅥

g. 𝅗𝅥 𝅗𝅥 𝅘𝅥 𝅝 𝅘𝅥 𝅘𝅥 𝅝 𝅗𝅥 = _____ 𝅗𝅥

h. 𝅘𝅥 𝅘𝅥 𝅗𝅥 = _____ 𝅗𝅥

i. 𝅗𝅥 𝅘𝅥 𝅘𝅥 𝅘𝅥 𝅘𝅥 𝅝 = _____ 𝅗𝅥

j. 𝅝 𝅘𝅥 𝅘𝅥 𝅗𝅥 𝅝 = _____ 𝅗𝅥

42

7. What is the sum in QUARTER NOTES of each of these?

a. ♩ ♩ ♩ ♩ = ___6___ ♩

b. ♩ ♩ 𝅝 = _____ ♩

c. 𝅝 ♩ ♩ = _____ ♩

d. ♩ ♩ ♩ ♩ = _____ ♩

e. ♩ 𝅝 ♩ ♩ = _____ ♩

f. 𝅝 ♩ ♩ ♩ ♩ = _____ ♩

g. ♩ ♩ ♩ ♩ 𝅝 = _____ ♩

h. ♩ ♩ ♩ = _____ ♩

i. ♩ ♩ 𝅝 ♩ ♩ = _____ ♩

j. ♩ ♩ 𝅝 = _____ ♩

8. Fill in the missing note.

a. ♩ + ♩ + _____ = 𝅝

b. ♩ + ♩ + _____ = 𝅝

c. ♩ + ♩ + ♩ + _____ = 𝅝

d. ♩ + _____ = ♩

A quarter note can be divided into two EIGHTH notes. ♩ = ♪ ♪ or ♫

A quarter rest can be divided into two EIGHTH rests. 𝄽 = ⁊ ⁊

EXERCISES

1. Fill in the missing note.

   a. ♩ + ♪ + _____ = ♩ (half note)

   b. ♩ (half) + ♩ + ♪ + _____ = 𝅝

   c. ♩ (half) + ♫♩ + _____ = 𝅝

   d. ♫♩ + _____ = ♩ (half)

   e. ♪ + ♪ + ♪ + _____ = ♩ (half)

   f. ♩ (half) + ♫♩ + ♪ + _____ = 𝅝

2. What is the sum in EIGHTH NOTES of each of these?

   a. ♩ = ___2___ ♪

   b. ♩ (half) = _____ ♪

   c. 𝅝 = _____ ♪

   d. ♩ ♪ = _____ ♪

   e. ♩ ♩ = _____ ♪

   f. ♫ ♩ = _____ ♪

   g. ♩ (half) ♪ = _____ ♪

   h. ♩ (half) ♩ (half) = _____ ♪

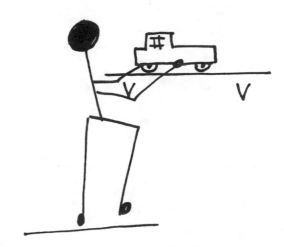

3. What is the sum in EIGHTH NOTES of each of these?

   a. ♩ (half) ♫♩ = _____ ♪

   b. ♩ (half) ♫♩ ♪ = _____ ♪

   c. ♩ (half) ♫ ♫♩ = _____ ♪

   d. ♩ (half) ♩ = _____ ♪

   e. ♩ ♪ ♩ = _____ ♪

   f. ♩ (half) ♩ ♪ = _____ ♪

   g. ♩ ♩ (half) ♫♩ = _____ ♪

   h. 𝅝 ♪ = _____ ♪

44

An eighth note can be divided into two SIXTEENTH notes. ♪ =  or

An eighth rest can be divided into two SIXTEENTH rests. ⅞ = ⅞ ⅞

so ♫ = ♪   and ♬♬ = ♫ = ♩

EXERCISES

1. What is the sum in SIXTEENTH NOTES of each of these?

a. ♪ = __2__ 𝅘𝅥𝅯

b. ♩ = _____ 𝅘𝅥𝅯

c. ♫ = _____ 𝅘𝅥𝅯

d. ♬ = _____ 𝅘𝅥𝅯

e. ♩ ♪ = _____ 𝅘𝅥𝅯

f. ♫ ♫ = _____ 𝅘𝅥𝅯

g. ♫ = _____ 𝅘𝅥𝅯

h. ♩ ♩ = _____ 𝅘𝅥𝅯

i. ♩ ♫ = _____ 𝅘𝅥𝅯

j. 𝅗𝅥 = _____ 𝅘𝅥𝅯

2. What is the sum in SIXTEENTH NOTES of each of these?

a. ♩ ♩ ♪ = _____ 𝅘𝅥𝅯

b. 𝅗𝅥 ♩ = _____ 𝅘𝅥𝅯

c. ♬♬ = _____ 𝅘𝅥𝅯

d. 𝅗𝅥 ♪ = _____ 𝅘𝅥𝅯

e. ♫ ♫ 𝅘𝅥𝅯 = _____ 𝅘𝅥𝅯

f. ♬♬ = _____ 𝅘𝅥𝅯

g. ♫ = _____ 𝅘𝅥𝅯

h. ♩ ♩ ♩ = _____ 𝅘𝅥𝅯

i. ♩ ♫ 𝅗𝅥 = _____ 𝅘𝅥𝅯

j. ♬ ♩ = _____ 𝅘𝅥𝅯

3. Fill in the missing note.

a. ♩ + ♫♫ + _____ = 𝅝

b. ♫♩ + ♫♩ + _____ = 𝅗𝅥

c. ♫♫ + _____ = 𝅗𝅥

d. ♩ + ♪ + ♪ + _____ = 𝅗𝅥

e. 𝅗𝅥 + ♫♩ + ♫♩ + _____ = 𝅝

f. ♫♫♩ + ♫♩ + _____ = 𝅗𝅥

g. ♪ + ♪ + _____ = 𝅗𝅥

h. ♪ + ♪ + ♫♩ + _____ = 𝅗𝅥

i. 𝅗𝅥 + ♫♫♫ + _____ = 𝅝

j. ♩ + ♫♩ + _____ = 𝅗𝅥

Each note and rest in these charts is twice the value of the next one down.

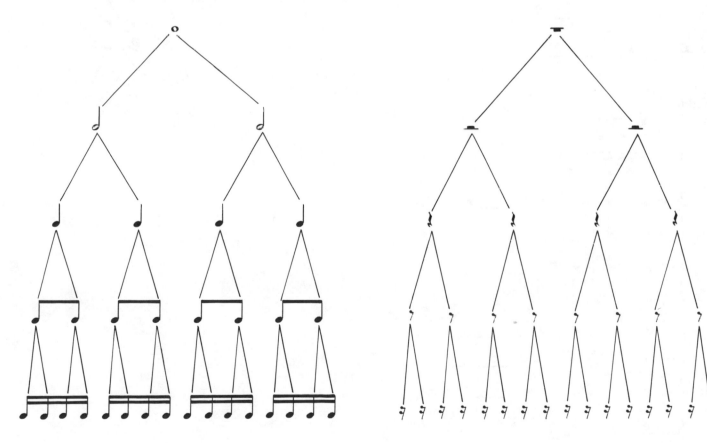

46

A DOT after a note or rest adds one half of the note's value to that note.

𝅝· = 𝅝 + 𝅗𝅥   𝄻· = 𝄻 + 𝄼

𝅗𝅥· = 𝅗𝅥 + 𝅘𝅥   𝄼· = 𝄼 + 𝄽

𝅘𝅥· = 𝅘𝅥 + 𝅘𝅥𝅮   𝄽· = 𝄽 + 𝄾

𝅘𝅥𝅮· = 𝅘𝅥𝅮 + 𝅘𝅥𝅯   𝄾· = 𝄾 + 𝄿

EXERCISES

1. Fill in the blanks.

a. 𝄾· = ___3___ 𝄿

b. 𝄽· = _____ 𝄾

c. 𝄼· = _____ 𝄽

d. 𝄽· 𝄾 = _____ 𝄼

e. 𝄾· 𝄾· = _____ 𝄿

f. 𝄽· 𝄾 𝄾 = _____ 𝄾

g. 𝄼 𝄼 = _____ 𝄽

h. 𝄽 𝄽 𝄽· = _____ 𝄾

i. 𝄾 𝄾 𝄾· = _____ 𝄿

j. 𝄽· 𝄾 𝄽 = _____ 𝄾

2. Fill in the blanks.

a. 𝅗𝅥· 𝅘𝅥𝅮 𝅘𝅥 𝅘𝅥 = ___3___ 𝅘𝅥

b. 𝅘𝅥 𝅘𝅥𝅯𝅘𝅥𝅯𝅘𝅥𝅯𝅘𝅥𝅯 𝅗𝅥· = _____ 𝅘𝅥

c. 𝅘𝅥𝅮𝅘𝅥𝅮 𝅘𝅥 𝅗𝅥· 𝅘𝅥𝅮 = _____ 𝅘𝅥

d. 𝅗𝅥· 𝅘𝅥 𝅗𝅥 = _____ 𝅗𝅥

e. 𝅘𝅥 𝅘𝅥 𝅗𝅥· 𝅘𝅥𝅮 = _____ 𝅗𝅥

f. 𝅘𝅥 𝅘𝅥 𝅗𝅥 𝅗𝅥· 𝅘𝅥 = _____ 𝅗𝅥

g. 𝅗𝅥· 𝅘𝅥𝅮 𝅗𝅥 𝅘𝅥 𝅘𝅥 = _____ 𝅗𝅥

h. 𝅗𝅥 𝅗𝅥· 𝅘𝅥 𝅘𝅥 𝅘𝅥 = _____ 𝅝

i. 𝅘𝅥 𝅘𝅥𝅮𝅘𝅥𝅮 𝅘𝅥 𝅗𝅥· 𝅘𝅥 = _____ 𝅝

j. 𝅗𝅥· 𝅘𝅥𝅮𝅗𝅥 𝅝 𝅗𝅥 𝅗𝅥 = _____ 𝅝

A TIE is another way of increasing the time value of a note. It is a curved line that joins 2 notes of the same pitch. It means that you do not play the second note but you hold the first note for the total value of both notes.

Notice that a curved line joining two notes that are *not* the same pitch is *not* a tie. This is usually a phrase or bowing mark.

These curved lines join the heads of the notes not the stems. So if the stems on the notes are going down, the line will curve above the notes. If the stems are going up, the line will curve below the notes.

EXERCISES

1. Put a circle around each note that is tied and not played.

2. Write one note or one dotted note that has the same total value:

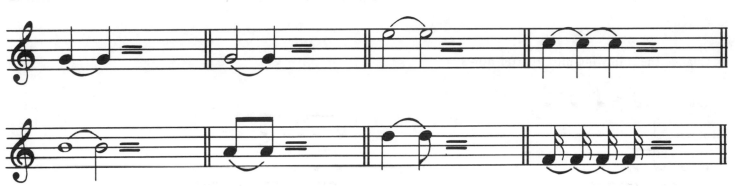

REVIEW EXERCISES

1. Write two notes that together have the same value as each of these notes.

a. 𝅗𝅥 =

b. ♩ =

c. o =

d. ♪ =

e. 𝅗𝅥. =

f. ♩. =

g. o· =

h. ♪. =

48

2. Fill in the missing note.

   a. ♩ + _____ = 𝅗𝅥

   b. 𝅗𝅥 + _____ = 𝅝

   c. 𝅗𝅥 + ♩ + _____ = 𝅗𝅥.

   d. 𝅗𝅥 + ♪ + _____ = 𝅗𝅥

   e. 𝅘𝅥𝅯𝅘𝅥𝅯𝅘𝅥𝅯 + _____ = ♩

   f. 𝅗𝅥   ♩ + _____ = 𝅝

   g. ♪ + _____ = ♩

   h. ♪ + 𝅘𝅥𝅯 + _____ = ♩

3. Write one note or one dotted note that has the same total value as:

   a. ♩ + ♩ =

   b. 𝅗𝅥 + 𝅗𝅥 =

   c. 𝅝 + 𝅗𝅥 =

   d. ♩ + ♩ + ♩ =

   e. 𝅗𝅥 + ♫ =

   f. ♫ + ♫ =

   g. ♩ + 𝅗𝅥 =

   h. 𝅗𝅥 + 𝅘𝅥𝅯𝅘𝅥𝅯𝅘𝅥𝅯𝅘𝅥𝅯 =

4. Write one rest or one dotted rest that has the same total value as:

   a. 𝄽   𝄽 =

   b. 𝄼   𝄽 =

   c. 𝄾   𝄾 =

   d. 𝄾   𝄿 =

   e. 𝄽   𝄾   𝄾 =

   f. 𝄼   𝄼 =

   g. 𝄿   𝄿   𝄾 =

   h. 𝄽   𝄾   𝄾 =

5. Change the following into quarter notes.

   example: 𝅗𝅥. = ♩ ♩ ♩

   a. 𝅗𝅥 𝅗𝅥 =

   b. 𝅗𝅥 ♫ =

   c. ♫ 𝅘𝅥𝅯𝅘𝅥𝅯𝅘𝅥𝅯 =

   d. 𝅘𝅥𝅯𝅘𝅥𝅯𝅘𝅥𝅯𝅘𝅥𝅯 ♫ 𝅗𝅥 =

   e. ♫ 𝅗𝅥 =

   f. ♫ ♫ 𝅘𝅥𝅯𝅘𝅥𝅯𝅘𝅥𝅯 =

6. Change the following into half notes.

   a. ♩ ♩ ♫ ♩ =

   b. ♫ ♫ ♩ ♩ =

   c. ♩ ♩ ♩ ♩ ♩ ♩ =

   d. 𝅘𝅥𝅯𝅘𝅥𝅯𝅘𝅥𝅯𝅘𝅥𝅯 ♩ ♫ ♫ =

   e. ♫ ♩ ♫ ♩ =

   f. 𝅝   ♩ ♫ =

7. Change the following into eighth notes using 'flags'.

a.   ♩   ♩   ♩ =

b.   ♩   ♩   ♩ =

c.   ♩   ♫♫ =

d.   ♩   ♩   ♩ =

e.   ♫♫   ♫♫ =

f.   ♩   ♩   ♫♫ =

8. Change the following into sixteenth notes using beams.

a.   ♫   ♫   ♩ =

b.   ♩   ♩ =

c.   ♩   ♫ =

d.   ♩   ♩ =

e.   ♫   ♫   ♫ =

f.   ♩   ♫ =

9. Fill in the blanks.

    a. 1 quarter note = 2 ___♪___ notes.

    b. 1 whole note = 2 _____ notes.

    c. 1 eighth rest = 2 _____ rests.

    d. 1 whole rest = 4 _____ rests.

    e. 1 quarter note = 4 _____ notes.

    f. 1 dotted half note = 3 _____ notes.

    g. 1 half rest = 2 _____ rests.

    h. 1 half note = 2 _____ notes.

    i. 1 eighth note = 2 _____ notes.

    j. 1 dotted quarter note = 3 _____ notes.

10. Fill in the blanks.

    a. 1 _____ rest = 2 eighth rests.

    b. 1 _____ note = 2 quarter notes.

    c. 1 _____ note = 2 half notes.

    d. 1 _____ rest = 4 eighth rests.

    e. 1 _____ rest = 3 sixteenth rests.

    f. 1 _____ note = 4 sixteenth notes.

    g. 1 _____ note = 3 quarter notes.

    h. 1 _____ rest = 2 sixteenth rests.

    i. 1 _____ note = 3 half notes.

    j. 1 _____ rest = 4 sixteenth rests.

NOTE WRITING

(crossword puzzle grid)

ACROSS

1. Two notes down from F.

3. Three notes up from C.

5. 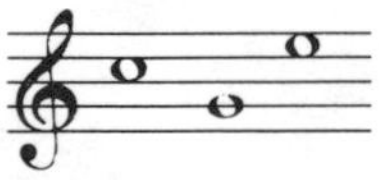 (musical notation) are _____ notes.

7. The bottom line in the treble clef.

8. Name these notes: (musical notation)

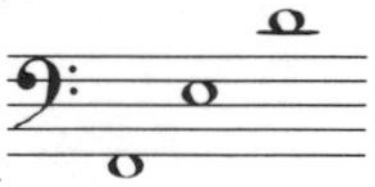

10. This is a _____

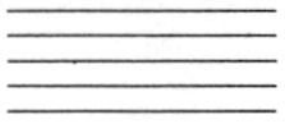

12. The treble clef shows you where _____ is.

13. This is a ♮

15. The next note down from C.

16. 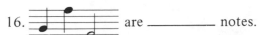 are _____ notes.

18. The next three notes up from F.

21. The top two spaces in the treble clef.

22. ⸮ is an _____ rest.

DOWN

2.  𝄞 is a treble _____ .

4. 𝄢 is a _____ clef.

6. 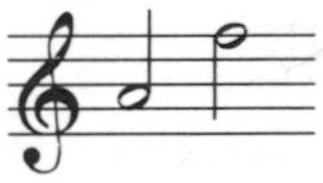 (musical notation) are _____ notes.

9.  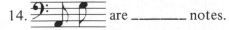 These notes move _____ .

11. Notes for the right hand are written in the _____ clef.

14. (musical notation) are _____ notes.

17.  ♩ is a _____ .

19. Middle C can be written in _____ clefs.

20. The first two leger lines above the treble clef.

CHAPTER 2

MAJOR SCALES

A SCALE is a series of notes whose names are in alphabetical order.

The notes of a scale are numbered from the bottom up and Roman numerals are used instead of ordinary numbers. That is

	I	II	III	IV	V	VI	VII	VIII or I
instead of	1	2	3	4	5	6	7	8 or l

All major scales have a special pattern of whole tones and semitones which occur in this order:

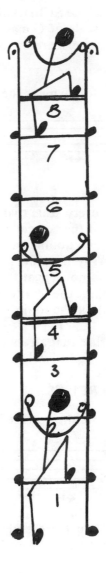

I		II		III	IV		V		VI		VII	VIII
	tone		tone	semitone		tone		tone		tone	semitone	

In other words there is a semitone between III and IV, and a semitone between VII and VIII but there are whole tones between each of the other degrees of the scale.

A major scale can start on any note but must follow the prescribed pattern of tones and semitones.

In any scale or key there are three notes that are more important than any of the others.
In order of importance they are:

the first note (I) which is called the KEY NOTE or TONIC
the fifth note (V) which is called the DOMINANT
the fourth note (IV) which is called the SUBDOMINANT

THE SCALE OF C MAJOR

To write the scale of C major start on C and write one note on each line and space until you get to the next C. Then mark where the semitones should be, (between III and IV, and VII and VIII.)

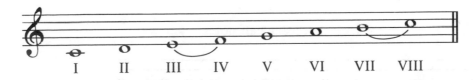

Check the distance from I to II, from II to III and so on. You will see that no sharps or flats are needed to make these notes fit the pattern for the major scale.

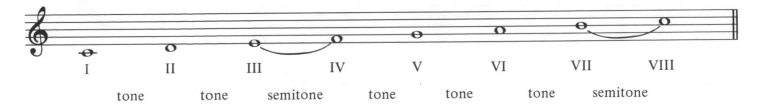

The TONIC of C major is C because C is the first note. The DOMINANT of C major is G because G is the fifth note. The SUBDOMINANT of C major is F because F is the fourth note.

The scale of C major is the only scale made up entirely of white notes. Every other major scale has to have at least one sharp or flat so that the pattern of tones and semitones will be right.

The following is the usual way to write a scale.

   I   IV   V   I   V   IV   I

For every scale that you write:
1. Put the correct clef at the beginning of the staff.
2. Put a double bar line at the end.
3. Write the scale ascending (going up) and descending (going down.)
4. Do not repeat the top note.
5. Mark the semitones with a slur.
6. Mark the tonic, subdominant and dominant notes.

Be sure that all six of these points are done.

EXERCISES

1. Write the correct Roman numeral under each note. Mark each semitone with a slur.

2. Write these scales. Mark each semitone with a slur and label each tonic, subdominant and dominant note by putting I, IV or V under them.

   (a)   C major ascending only in the treble clef, using whole notes.

   (b)   C major ascending only in the bass clef, using half notes.

   (c)   C major descending only in the bass clef, using quarter notes.

   (d)   C major ascending and descending in the treble clef, using half notes.

MAJOR SCALES THAT HAVE SHARPS,

THE SCALE OF G MAJOR.

To write the scale of G major start on G and write a note on every line and space until you get to the next G. Mark where the semitones should be (between III and IV, and VII and VIII).

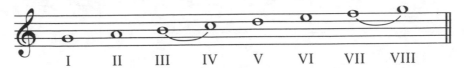

I   II   III   IV   V   VI   VII   VIII

Check the distance between each note and its neighbour to see if the order of whole tones and semitones is the right one for a major scale.
All the distances between I, II, III, IV, V and VI are correct. When you come to VI and VII you will find that they are only a semitone apart. According to the scale pattern there must be a whole tone between VI and VII so you will have to raise the F to an F sharp. The distance between VII and VIII is now a semitone, which is correct.

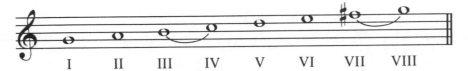

I   II   III   IV   V   VI   VII   VIII

The scale pattern is now correct, so the scale of G major and the key of G major always have an F sharp.

Instead of writing a sharp in front of every F in a piece in G major, the sharp is usually written at the beginning of the staff right after the clef sign, showing that ALL the F's no matter where they are on the staff are to be raised to F♯'s. This is called a KEY SIGNATURE.

This is the key signature of G major. Notice where the F♯ is in each clef.

Here is the scale of G major written with its key signature instead of an accidental.

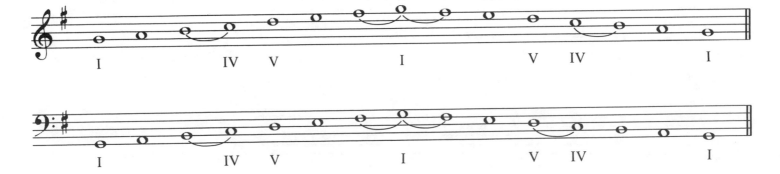

I   IV V   I   V IV   I

I   IV V   I   V IV   I

The tonic of G major is G. The dominant of G major is D. The subdominant of G major is C.

EXERCISES

1. Mark where the semitones should occur to make this a major scale. Then add the correct accidental to the correct note to make it the scale of G major. Label each tonic, subdominant and dominant note.

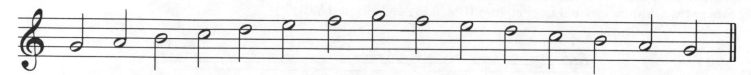

2. Write the key signature of G major in each bar.

3. Write these scales using the correct accidental instead of a key signature. Mark each semitone with a slur and label the tonic and dominant notes.

   (a)   G major ascending in the bass clef using half notes.

   (b)   G major ascending in the treble clef using quarter notes.

   (c)   G major descending in the treble clef using whole notes.

   (d)   G major descending in the bass clef using eighth notes.

4. Write these scales using the correct key signature. Mark each semitone with a slur and label each tonic note.

   (a)   G major descending in the bass clef using quarter notes.

(b) G major ascending in the treble clef using dotted half notes.

(c) G major ascending in the bass clef using whole notes.

(d) G major descending in the treble clef using half notes.

5. Write the scale of G major ascending and descending in the treble clef in whole notes using the correct key signature.

6. Write the scale of G major ascending and descending in the bass clef in quarter notes using accidentals instead of a key signature.

7. Write the dominant of G major in the treble clef, and the tonic of G major in the bass clef using the correct key signature.

THE SCALE OF D MAJOR

To write the scale of D major start on D and write one note in each line and space until you get to the next D. Mark where the semitones should be.

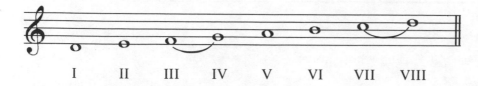

I   II   III   IV   V   VI   VII   VIII

Look at the distance between each note and the next one.

From D to E is a whole tone. Therefore E is correct.
From E to F is a semitone, and should be a tone. Therefore you must raise the F to F sharp.
From F♯ to G is a semitone. Therefore G is correct.
From G to A is a tone. Therefore A is correct.
From A to B is a tone. Therefore B is correct.
From B to C is a semitone and should be a tone. Therefore you must raise the C to C♯.
From C♯ to D is a semitone. Therefore D is correct.

I   II   III   IV   V   VI   VII   VIII

So the scale of D major and the key of D major have two sharps — F♯ and C♯.

The sharps in a key signature always go in the same order. F♯ (from the key signature of G major) is always the first one, and now we add C♯ to make the key signature of D major. C♯ is always the second sharp in a key signature. Here is the key signature of D major:

Here is the scale of D major written with its key signature. Each semitone is marked with a slur, and each tonic, subdominant and dominant note is labelled.

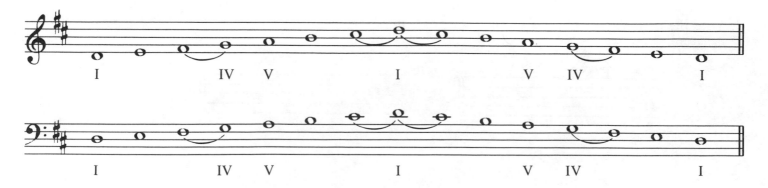

I   IV   V   I   V   IV   I

I   IV   V   I   V   IV   I

The tonic of D major is D. The dominant of D major is A. The subdominant of D major is G.

EXERCISES

1. Write the key signature and the tonic note of D major in each bar.

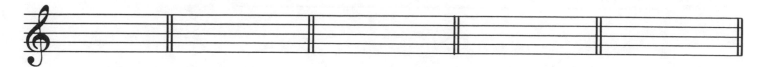

2. Write the key signature and the dominant note of D major in each bar.

3. Write these scales using accidentals instead of a key signature. Mark each semitone with a slur and label the dominant note.

   (a) D major ascending in the treble clef in eighth notes.

   (b) D major descending in the treble clef in half notes.

   (c) D major descending in the bass clef in whole notes.

   (d) D major ascending in the bass clef in quarter notes.

4. Write these scales using the correct key signature. Mark each semitone with a slur and label the subdominant note.

   (a) D major ascending in the bass clef in half notes.

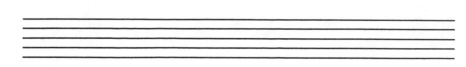

58

(b)　D major descending in the bass clef in dotted half notes.

(c)　D major descending in the treble clef in quarter notes.

(d)　D major ascending in the treble clef in whole notes.

5. Write the scale of D major ascending and descending in the treble clef in half notes using the correct key signature.

6. Write the scale of D major ascending and descending in the bass clef in quarter notes using accidentals instead of a key signature.

GENERAL METHOD FOR WRITING ANY MAJOR SCALE.

1. Write a series of eight notes upwards (ascending) from I to I and back down (descending). Write the top note ONCE only. Count the number of notes you have written. There should be 15.

2. Add Roman numerals if needed.

3. Mark the semitones between III and IV, and VII and VIII up and down.

4. Starting at the bottom check the distance between each note and its neighbour and add accidentals where necessary or the correct key signature.

THE SCALE OF A MAJOR

To write the scale of A major start on A and write a note on each space and line until you get to the next A. Mark where the semitones should be.

If you check the distance between each note and the next, as you did in the scale of D major, you will find that the scale of A major needs three sharps in order to have the correct pattern of whole tones and semitones.

So the scale of A major and the key of A major have three sharps: F♯, C♯ and G♯. To write its key signature write the two sharps you already know and add the G♯. G♯ is always the third sharp in a key signature.

Here is the scale of A major written with its key signature instead of accidentals.

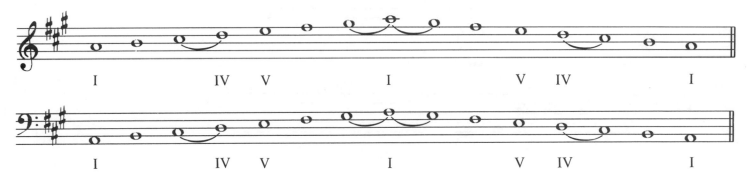

The tonic of A major is A. The dominant of A major is E. The subdominant of A major is D.

EXERCISES

1. Add the correct accidentals to make the scale of A major.

2. Write the key signature and the tonic of A major in each bar.

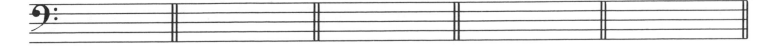

3. Write the key signature and the dominant of A major in each bar.

4. Write these scales using the correct key signature. Mark each semitone and label each tonic and dominant note.

   (a)   A major ascending in the treble clef in half notes.

   (b)   A major descending in the bass clef in quarter notes.

   (c)   A major ascending in the bass clef in whole notes.

   (d)   A major descending in the treble clef in eighth notes.

5. Write these scales using accidentals instead of a key signature. Mark each semitone and label each tonic and sub-dominant note.

   (a)   A major ascending in the bass clef in half notes.

   (b)   A major ascending in the treble clef in quarter notes.

(c) A major descending in the bass clef in eighth notes.

(d) A major descending in the treble clef in whole notes.

6. Write the scale of A major ascending and descending in whole notes in the bass clef using the correct key signature. Mark each semitone with a slur and label each tonic, subdominant and dominant note.

7. Write the scale of A major in the treble clef in quarter notes using accidentals instead of a key signature. Mark each semitone with a slur and label each tonic and dominant note.

For extra practice:

THE SCALE OF E MAJOR

To write the scale of E major start on E and write one note on each line and space until you get to the next E. Mark where the semitones should be

I II III IV V VI VII VIII

If you check the distance between each note and the next, as you did in the other scales, you will find that E major needs four sharps in order to have the correct pattern of whole tones and semitones.

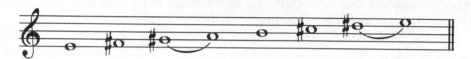

So the scale of E major and the key of E major have four sharps — F♯. C♯, G♯ and D♯. To write the key signature for E, write the three sharps used for A major and add the new D♯. D♯ is always the fourth sharp in a key signature.

Here is the scale of E major written with its key signature.

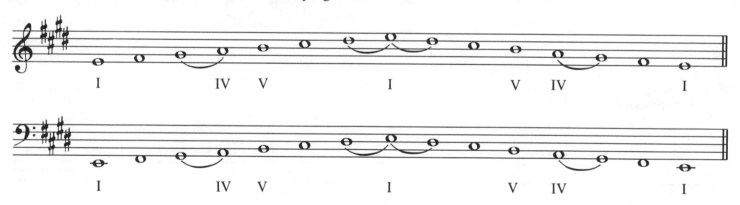

I IV V I V IV I

I IV V I V IV I

The tonic of E major is E. The dominant of E major is B. The subdominant of E major is A.

EXERCISES

1. Add the correct accidentals to make the scale of E major. Mark each semitone with a slur.

2. Write in each bar the key signature and the tonic, subdominant and dominant notes of E major.

3. Write these scales using the correct key signature. Mark each semitone with a slur and label the subdominant and dominant notes.

   (a)   E major ascending in the bass clef in quarter notes.

   (b)   E major descending in the treble clef in half notes.

   (c)   E major descending in the treble clef in whole notes.

   (d)   E major ascending in the bass clef in eighth notes.

4. Write these scales using accidentals instead of a key signature. Mark each semitone with a slur and label the tonic, subdominant and dominant notes.

   (a)   E major ascending in the bass clef in half notes.

   (b)   E major ascending in the treble clef in whole notes.

64

(c) E major descending in the treble clef in eighth notes.

(d) E major descending in the bass clef in quarter notes.

5. Write the scale of E major ascending and descending in the treble clef in half notes. Mark each semitone with a slur and label each tonic and dominant note.

6. Write the scale of E major ascending and descending in the bass clef in quarter notes using accidentals instead of a key signature. Mark each semitone with a slur and label each tonic and subdominant note.

For extra practice:

You will probably not learn the major scales that have more than four sharps until you are ready for more advanced work, but in case you need them, here they are:

B major has 5 sharps.

F♯ major has 6 sharps.

C♯ major has 7 sharps.

Here is a complete list of the major scales that have sharps.

G major has 1 sharp: F♯
D major has 2 sharps: F♯ C♯
A major has 3 sharps: F♯ C♯ G♯
E major has 4 sharps: F♯ C♯ G♯ D♯
B major has 5 sharps: F♯ C♯ G♯ D♯ A♯
F♯ major has 6 sharps: F♯ C♯ G♯ D♯ A♯ E♯
C♯ major has 7 sharps: F♯ C♯ G♯ D♯ A♯ E♯ B♯

This little sentence has been used for many years to help students remember the order of the sharps in a key signature:

Father Charles Goes Down And Ends Battle. F C G D A E B

Fat Cat Gets Down At Every Beat

REVIEW EXERCISES FOR MAJOR SCALES THAT HAVE SHARPS.

1. Add the correct clef and accidentals to form these scales.

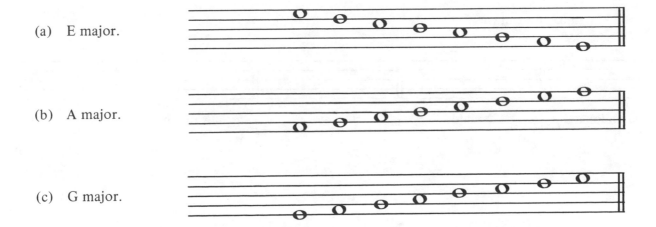

(a)   E major.

(b)   A major.

(c)   G major.

2. Write these scales ascending and descending in the treble clef using the correct key signature for each.

(a) G major.

(b) A major.

(c) D major.

3. Write these scales ascending and descending in the bass clef using accidentals instead of a key signature.

(a) E major.

(b) D major.

(c) G major.

4. Write the key signature and the tonic note of:

G major   D major   C major   A major   E major.

5. Write the key signature and the dominant note of:

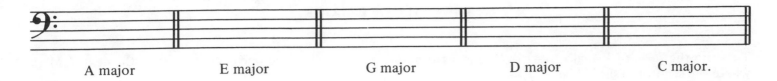

     A major   E major   G major   D major   C major.

6. Write the key signature and the subdominant note of:

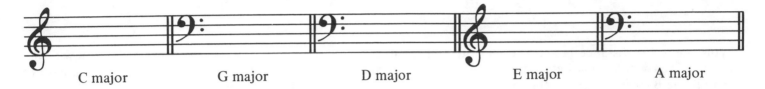

     C major   G major   D major   E major   A major

MAJOR SCALES THAT HAVE FLATS.

THE SCALE OF F MAJOR.

To write the scale of F major start on F and write a note on each space and line until you get to the next F. Mark where the semitones should be.

If you check the distance between each note and the next, as you have been doing in the other scales, you will find that there is a whole tone between A and B. Since you must have a semitone between III and IV you will have to LOWER the B to B♭. That is the only note that needs to be altered in the scale of F.

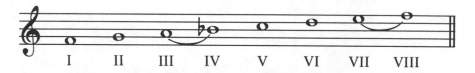

So the scale of F major and the key of F major have one flat: B♭.
Here is the key signature of F major.

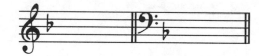

Here is the scale of F major written with its key signature.

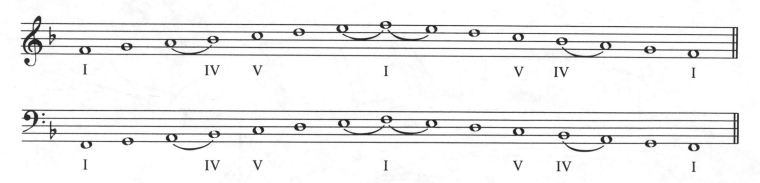

The tonic of F major is F. The dominant of F major is C. The subdominant of F major is B♭.

EXERCISES

1. Add an accidental to the correct note to make the scale of F major. Mark each semitone with a slur and label each tonic, subdominant and dominant note.

2. Write these scales using the correct key signature. Mark each semitone with a slur and label each tonic note.

(a) F major ascending in the treble clef in half notes.

(b) F major ascending in the bass clef in whole notes.

(c) F major descending in the bass clef in quarter notes.

(d) F major descending in the treble clef in eighth notes.

3. Write these scales using an accidental instead of a key signature.

(a) F major descending in the bass clef in whole notes.

(b) F major ascending in the treble clef in half notes.

70

(c) F major ascending in the bass clef in eighth notes.

(d) F major descending in the treble clef in whole notes.

4. Write the scale of F major ascending and descending in the bass clef in half notes. Mark each semitone with a slur and label each subdominant and dominant note.

5. Write the scale of F major ascending and descending in the treble clef in whole notes without using a key signature. Mark each semitone with a slur and label each tonic, subdominant and dominant note.

For extra practice:

THE SCALE OF B FLAT MAJOR.

To write the scale of B♭ major start on B and write a note on each line and space until you get to the next B. Put a flat in front of both the bottom B and the top B. Mark where the semitones should be.

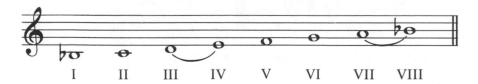

I   II   III   IV   V   VI   VII   VIII

Now check the distance between each note and the next and you will find that you must put a flat before E to make a semitone between III and IV.

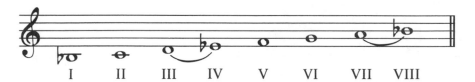

I   II   III   IV   V   VI   VII   VIII

So the scale of B♭ major and the key of B♭ major have two flats — B♭ and E♭. Here is the key signature of B♭ major.

The flats in a key signature always go in the same order. B♭ (from the key signature of F major) is always the first one, and now we have added E♭ which is always the second one.

Here is the scale of B♭ major written with its key signature.

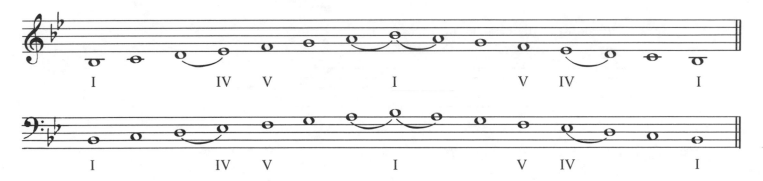

I   IV   V   I   V   IV   I

I   IV   V   I   V   IV   I

The tonic of B♭ major is B♭. The dominant of B♭ major is F. The subdominant of B♭ major is E♭.

EXERCISES

1. Add the correct accidentals to make the scale of B♭ major. Mark each semitone with a slur.

72

2. Write the key signature and the tonic note of B♭ major in each bar.

3. Write the key signature and the dominant note of B♭ major in each bar.

4. Write these scales using the correct key signature. Mark each semitone with a slur and label the tonic and sub-dominant notes.

   (a) B♭ major ascending in the treble clef in half notes.

   (b) B♭ major ascending in the bass clef in sixteenth notes.

   (c) B♭ major descending in the bass clef in whole notes.

   (d) B♭ major descending in the treble clef in eighth notes.

5. Write these scales using accidentals instead of a key signature. Mark each semitone with a slur and label each tonic note.

   (a) B♭ major descending in the treble clef in quarter notes.

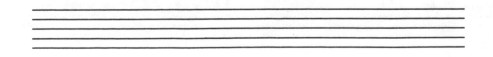

(b) Bb major descending in the bass clef in eighth notes.

(c) Bb major ascending in the bass clef in whole notes.

(d) Bb major ascending in the treble clef in sixteenth notes.

6. Write the scale of Bb major ascending and descending in the treble clef in half notes using the correct key signature. Mark each semitone with a slur and label each dominant note.

7. Write the scale of Bb major ascending and descending in the bass clef in quarter notes using accidentals instead of a key signature. Mark each semitone with a slur and label each subdominant note.

THE SCALE OF E FLAT MAJOR.

To write the scale of E♭ major start on E and write a note on each line and space until you get to the next E. Put a flat in front of each E, and mark where the semitones should be.

I II III IV V VI VII VIII

Now check the distance between each note and its neighbour and you will find it is necessary to put a flat before both the A and the B in order to get the correct pattern of tones and semitones.

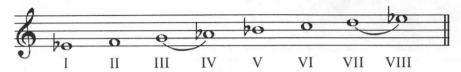

I II III IV V VI VII VIII

So the scale of E♭ major and the key of E♭ major have three flats — B♭, E♭ and A♭. Here is the key signature of E♭ major. Notice that the A♭ is added to the two flats that you already know.

Here is the scale of E♭ major written with its key signature.

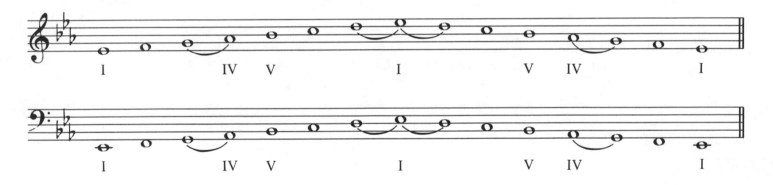

I   IV V   I   V IV   I

I   IV V   I   V IV   I

The tonic of E♭ major is E♭. The dominant of E♭ major is B♭.
The subdominant of E♭ major is A♭.

EXERCISES

1. Add the correct accidentals to make the scale of E♭ major. Mark each semitone with a slur.

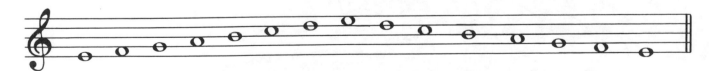

2. Write the key signature and the tonic note of E♭ major in each bar.

3. Write these scales using the correct key signature. Mark each semitone and label the subdominant and dominant notes.

   (a)   E♭ major descending in the bass clef in whole notes.

   (b)   E♭ major ascending in the treble clef in half notes.

   (c)   E♭ major ascending in the bass clef in eighth notes.

   (d)   E♭ major descending in the treble clef in quarter notes.

4. Write these scales using accidentals instead of a key signature. Mark each semitone with a slur and label each tonic and dominant note.

   (a)   E♭ major ascending in the treble clef in whole notes.

   (b)   E♭ major ascending in the bass clef in quarter notes.

76

(c) E♭ major descending in the bass clef in eighth notes.

(d) E♭ major descending in the treble clef in sixteenth notes.

5. Write the scale of E♭ major ascending and descending in the treble clef using accidentals instead of a key signature. Mark each semitone with a slur and label each tonic, subdominant and dominant note.

6. Write the scale of E♭ major ascending and descending in the bass clef using the correct key signature. Mark each semitone with a slur and label each tonic, subdominant and dominant note.

For extra practice:

THE SCALE OF A FLAT MAJOR.

To write the scale of A♭ major start on A and write a note on each line and space until you get to the next A. Put a flat in front of each A and mark where the semitones should be.

I   II   III   IV   V   VI   VII   VIII

Check the distance between each note as you have done with the other scales and you will find it is necessary to put a flat before the B, the D and the E.

I   II   III   IV   V   VI   VII   VIII

So the scale of A♭ major and the key of A♭ major have four flats — B♭, E♭, A♭ and D♭. Here is the key signature of A♭ major. The D♭ is added to the three flats that you have already learned.

Here is the scale of A♭ major written with its key signature.

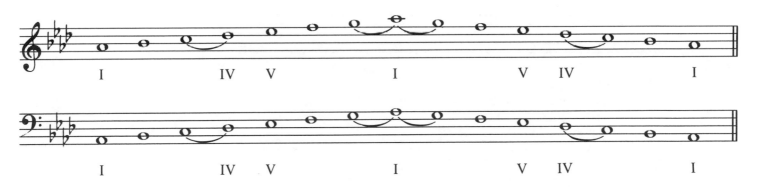

I   IV   V   I   V   IV   I

I   IV   V   I   V   IV   I

The tonic of A♭ major is A♭. The dominant of A♭ major is E♭. The subdominant of A♭ major is D♭.

EXERCISES

1. Add the correct accidentals to make the scale of A♭ major. Mark each semitone with a slur.

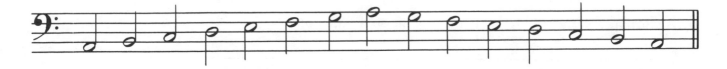

2. Write the key signature and the dominant note of A♭ major in each bar.

3. Write these scales using accidentals instead of a key signature. Mark each semitone with a slur and label the tonic and dominant notes.

   (a) A♭ major ascending in the bass clef in sixteenth notes.

   (b) A♭ major ascending in the treble clef in quarter notes.

   (c) A♭ major descending in the bass clef in whole notes.

   (d) A♭ major descending in the treble clef in eighth notes.

4. Write these scales using the correct key signature. Mark each semitone and label the subdominant note.

   (a) A♭ major descending in the bass clef in half notes.

   (b) A♭ major descending in the treble clef in sixteenth notes.

(c) Ab major ascending in the treble clef in whole notes.

(d) Ab major ascending in the bass clef in eighth notes.

5. Write the scale of Ab major ascending and descending in the bass clef using the correct key signature. Mark each semitone with a slur and label each tonic, subdominant and dominant note.

6. Write the scale of Ab major ascending and descending in the treble clef using accidentals instead of a key signature. Mark each semitone with a slur and label each tonic, subdominant and dominant note.

For extra practice:

REVIEW EXERCISES FOR ALL MAJOR SCALES.

1. Write the key signature and the subdominant note of:

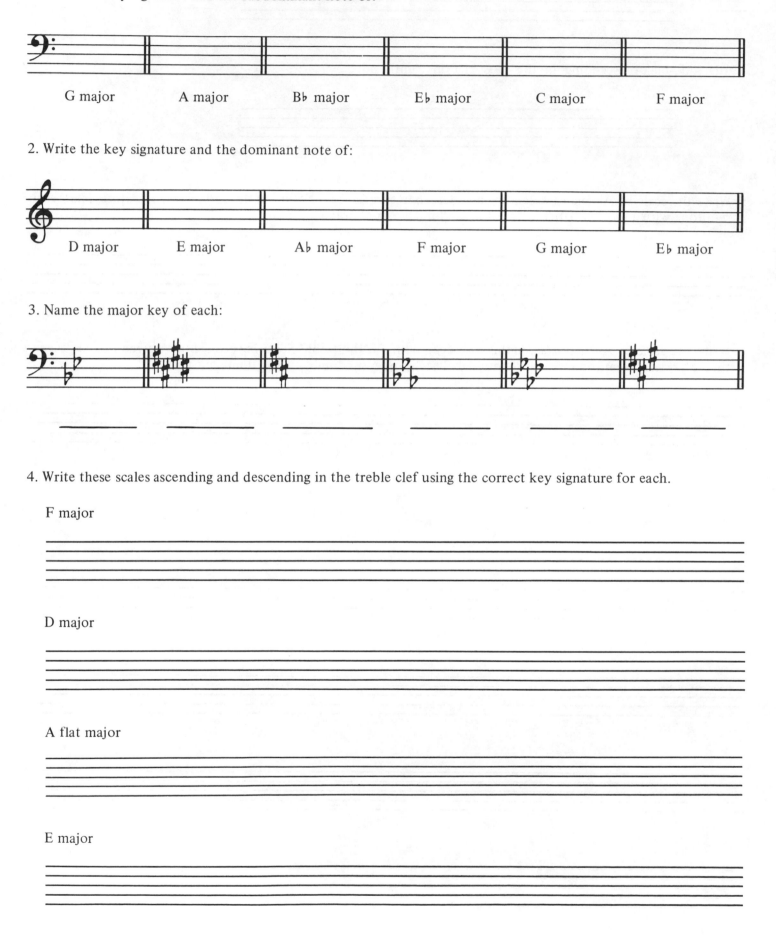

2. Write the key signature and the dominant note of:

3. Name the major key of each:

4. Write these scales ascending and descending in the treble clef using the correct key signature for each.

F major

D major

A flat major

E major

5. Add the tonic note to each of these bars.

6. Add the dominant note to each of these bars.

7. Add the subdominant note to each of these bars.

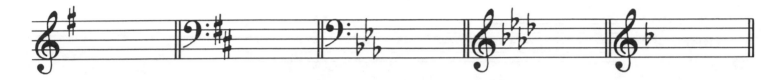

8. Write these scales ascending and descending in the bass clef using accidentals instead of a key signature.

E flat major

G major

A major

B flat major

82

9. Add the correct clef and accidentals to form these scales.

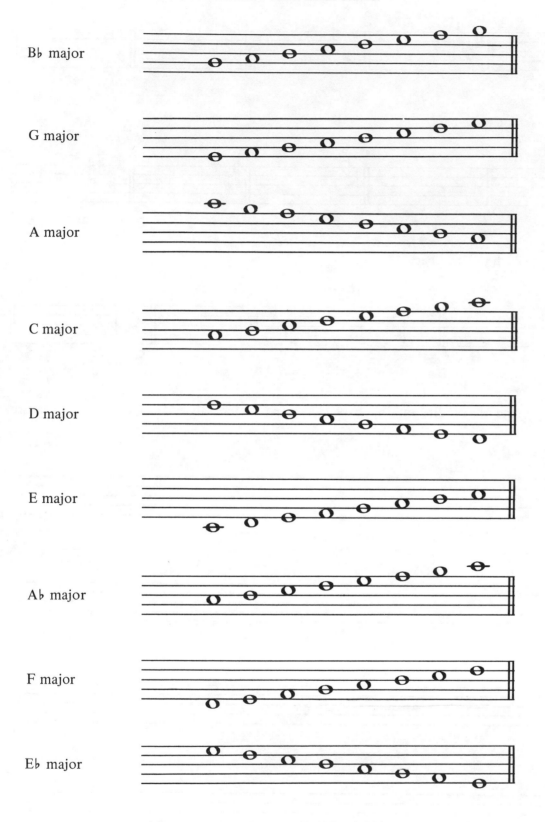

Bb major

G major

A major

C major

D major

E major

Ab major

F major

Eb major

10. Fill in the blanks.

    a.   the key signature of G major is _____

    b.   the dominant of A major is _____

    c.   the key whose key signature is three flats is _____

    d.   the key whose subdominant is D is _____

    e.   the first four sharps in a key signature are _____

    f.   the key signature of Ab major is _____

    g.   the tonic note of F major is _____

    h.   the third flat in a key signature is always _____

    i.   the subdominant of Ab major is _____

    j.   the key whose key signature is two sharps is _____

    k.   the dominant of Bb major is _____

    l.   the second sharp in a key signature is always _____

    m.   the key signature of E major is _____

    n.   the key whose dominant is E is _____

    o.   the key whose key signature is four flats is _____

    p.   the dominant of Eb major is _____

    q.   the tonic of G major is _____

    r.   the first four flats in a key signature are _____

    s.   the key whose tonic is Bb is _____

    t.   the subdominant of F major is _____

84

Here are examples of the major scales that have more than four flats, which you will learn later.

Db major has 5 flats:

Gb major has 6 flats:

Cb major has 7 flats:

Here is a complete list of the major scales that have flats.

F major has 1 flat: Bb

Bb major has 2 flats: Bb Eb

Eb major has 3 flats: Bb Eb Ab

Ab major has 4 flats: Bb Eb Ab Db

Db major has 5 flats: Bb Eb Ab Db Gb

Gb major has 6 flats: Bb Eb Ab Db Gb Cb

Cb major has 7 flats: Bb Eb Ab Db Gb Cb Fb

The sentence which helps you to remember the "order of the SHARPS" in sharp key signatures was:

Father Charles Goes Down And Ends Battle.

If you read it backwards you get:

Battle Ends And Down Goes Charles' Father; – this is the sentence which helps you to remember the "order of the FLATS" in flat key signatures.   B E A D G C F

Bead   Greatest Common Factor

?

1. This key has three flats. What key is it? _____

2. This key has an F sharp and a C sharp. What key is it? _____

3. This key does not have any flats or sharps. What key is it? _____

4. This key is called A flat major. What is the name of the third flat? _____

5. In A major what is the name of the sharp that is on a line? _____

6. This key has one flat more than the key of F major. What is its name? _____

7. This key signature has one sharp less than the key signature of D major. What is the key? _____

8. This key signature has two sharps in spaces and two sharps on lines. What is its name? _____

9. This key has three sharps. What is the name of its dominant? _____

10. This key has one sharp more than A major. What is its tonic note? _____

CHAPTER 3

MINOR SCALES

Like the major scale, a minor scale can start on any note and has eight notes in alphabetical order. These notes are numbered just like the major scale starting at the bottom.
The first note is the tonic, the fourth note is the subdominant and the fifth note is the dominant.

There are two kinds of minor scales — HARMONIC MINOR and MELODIC MINOR.

Play these two scales listening carefully to the differences between them.

The scale of E minor HARMONIC:

The scale of E minor MELODIC:

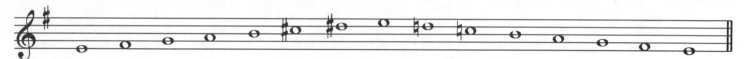

Notice that each of these scales has the same key signature as G major.

G major is called the RELATIVE MAJOR of E minor.
E minor is called the RELATIVE MINOR of G major.

Every minor scale shares the key signature of one of the major scales and is then 'related' to it.

In order to know the key signature of a minor scale you must know how to find its relative major.

TO FIND THE RELATIVE MAJOR OF ANY MINOR KEY:

1. Go up from I to III, that is to the third letter name of the minor scale.
2. Use the kind of III that is three semitones up from I.

Example: To find the relative major of C minor:–
1. From I up to III is C to E. So E is the letter name.
2. The kind of E that is three semitones up from C is E♭.
Therefore the relative major is E♭ major. C minor and E♭ major will use the same key signature of three flats.

TO FIND THE RELATIVE MINOR OF ANY MAJOR KEY:

1. Go down from I to VI, that is to the sixth letter name of the major scale.
2. Use the kind of VI that is three semitones down from I.

Example: To find the relative minor of F major:–
1. From I down to VI is F to D. So D is the letter name.
2. The kind of D that is three semitones down from F is D♮.
Therefore the relative minor of F major is D minor. D minor and F major will use the same key signature of one flat.

Perhaps this will help you remember whether to go up or down to find the relative major or minor. There are two friends. One is a Major in the army and the other is a coal miner. If the major wants to see the miner he has to go DOWN into the mine, and if the miner wants to see the major he has to go UP out of the mine.

EXERCISES

1. Name the relative minor of these major keys.

D major _____   B♭ major _____

E♭ major _____   C major _____

G major _____   F major _____

E major _____   A♭ major _____

2. Name the relative major of these minor keys.

E minor _____   C♯ minor _____

G minor _____   F minor _____

F♯ minor _____   B minor _____

C minor _____   D minor _____

3. Write the key signature of each of these minor keys.

G-   C♯-   F-   B-   E-   D-   C-   F♯-

4. Name the major and minor keys that have these key signatures.

major: _____ _____ _____ _____ _____ _____ _____

minor: _____ _____ _____ _____ _____ _____ _____

When a major scale and a minor scale share the SAME TONIC they are called the TONIC MAJOR and TONIC MINOR. C major is the tonic major of C minor. G minor is the tonic minor of G major and so on.

88

EXERCISES

1. Name the tonic minor of each of these keys and write the minor key signature.

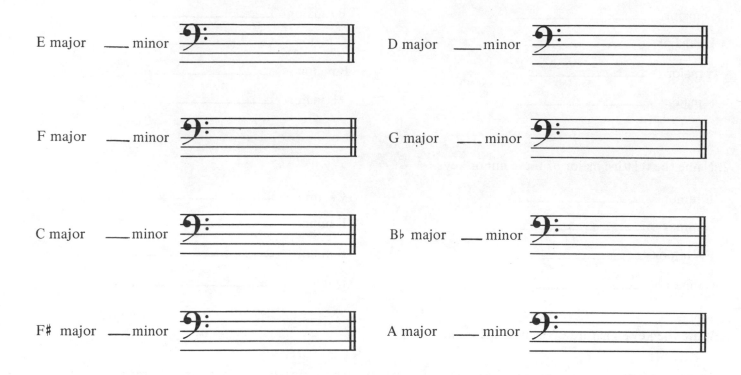

E major ___ minor

D major ___ minor

F major ___ minor

G major ___ minor

C major ___ minor

B♭ major ___ minor

F♯ major ___ minor

A major ___ minor

2. Name the tonic major of each of these keys and write the major key signature.

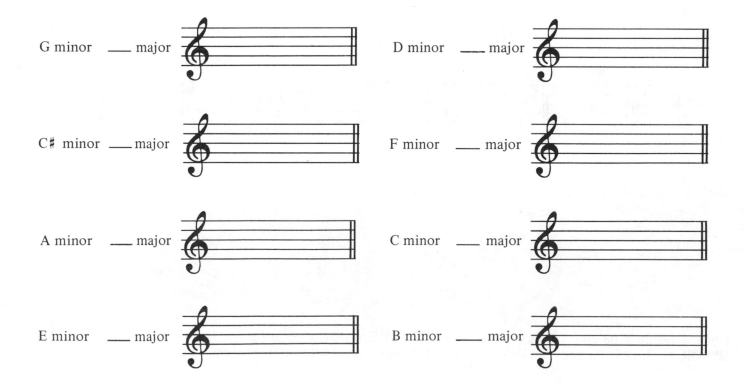

G minor ___ major

D minor ___ major

C♯ minor ___ major

F minor ___ major

A minor ___ major

C minor ___ major

E minor ___ major

B minor ___ major

HARMONIC MINOR SCALES.

The HARMONIC MINOR scale has this pattern:

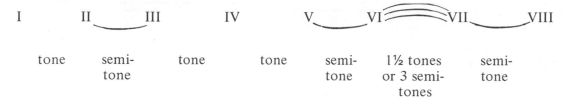

	I	II	III	IV	V	VI	VII	VIII
tone								

tone   semi-tone   tone   tone   semi-tone   1½ tones or 3 semi-tones   semi-tone

In other words there are semitones between II and III, V and VI, and VII and VIII, with a tone and a half between VI and VII, and whole tones between I and II, III and IV, and IV and V.

To write a harmonic minor scale using a key signature —

1. Write a series of notes from tonic up to tonic and down again.
2. Find the relative major and its key signature.
3. Add this key signature.
4. RAISE THE SEVENTH NOTE one semitone by adding the proper accidental.

Example: the scale of G minor harmonic, following the above four steps.

2. The relative major of G minor is Bb major, so G minor has 2 flats.

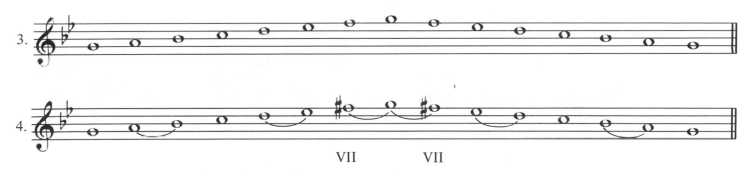

Notice that the notes of the harmonic minor scale are exactly the same ascending and descending.

To write a harmonic minor scale using accidentals instead of a key signature: —

1. Write the series of notes from tonic up to tonic and down again.
2. Find the relative major and its key signature.
3. Using the sharps or flats in this key signature change the notes that would have been affected by this key signature.
4. RAISE THE SEVENTH NOTE one semitone by adding the proper accidental.

Example: the scale of G minor harmonic, following the above four steps.

2. The relative major of G minor is Bb major so G minor has two flats.

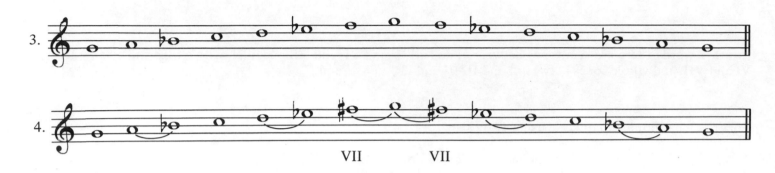

MELODIC MINOR SCALES

The MELODIC MINOR scale has this pattern:

Ascending:

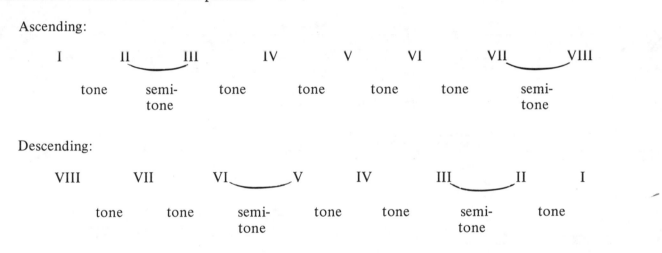

In the ascending scale the semitones are between II and III, and VII and VIII; in the descending scale the semitones are between VI and V, and III and II, so the scale does not sound the same coming down as it did going up.

To write a melodic minor scale using a key signature: —

1. Write a series of eight notes from tonic up to tonic and down again.
2. Find the relative major and its key signature.
3. Add this key signature.
4. Ascending: RAISE THE SIXTH AND SEVENTH NOTES one semitone each.
   Descending: RETURN THEM TO THEIR ORIGINAL PITCH according to the key signature by lowering them one semitone each.

Example: the scale of B minor melodic, following the above four steps.

1.

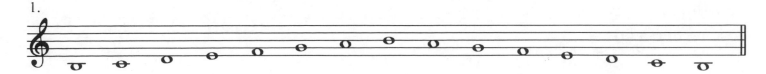

2. The relative of B minor is D major so B minor has two sharps.

3.

4.

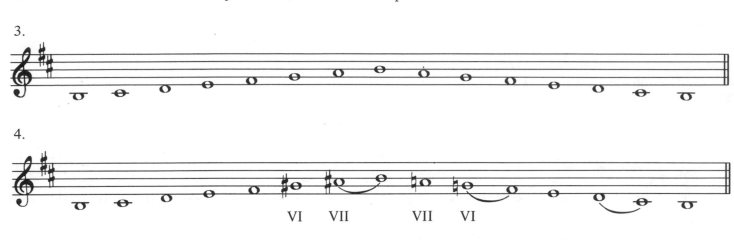

To write a melodic minor scale using accidentals instead of a key signature.

1. Write a series of notes from tonic up to tonic and down again.
2. Find the relative major and its key signature.
3. Using the sharps or flats in this signature change the notes that would have been affected by this key signature.
4. Ascending: RAISE THE SIXTH AND SEVENTH NOTES one semitone each by adding the proper accidentals.
   Descending: RETURN THEM TO THEIR ORIGINAL PITCH by adding the proper accidentals to lower them one semitone each.

Example: the scale of B minor melodic, following the above four steps.

1.

2. The relative major of B minor is D major so B minor has two sharps.

3.

4.

THE SCALE OF A MINOR.

The relative major of A minor is C major because

    1. I to III is A to C.
    2. three semitones up from A is C♮.

So the key signature of A minor is the same as that of C major: no sharps or flats.

The tonic of A minor is A. The dominant of A minor is E. The subdominant of A minor is D.

To write the scale of A minor harmonic —
1. Write the notes from A up to A and down again.
2. Raise the seventh note G one semitone by adding a sharp both ascending and descending.

To write the scale of A minor melodic —
1. Write the notes from A up to A and down again.
2. Ascending: Raise the sixth note F one semitone to F♯ and the seventh note G one semitone to G♯.
    Descending: Lower the same two notes by adding naturals.

EXERCISES

1. Add the correct accidental to make the scale of A minor harmonic.

2. Add the correct accidentals to make the scale of A minor melodic.

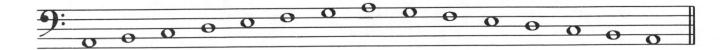

3. Write the scale of A minor harmonic ascending in the treble clef in half notes. Mark each semitone with a slur and label the tonic, subdominant and dominant notes.

4. Write the scale of A minor harmonic descending in the bass clef in whole notes. Mark each semitone with a slur and label the tonic, subdominant and dominant notes.

5. Write the scale of A minor harmonic ascending and descending in the treble clef in eighth notes.

6. Write the scale of A minor melodic ascending and descending in the bass clef in quarter notes. Mark each semitone with a slur and label each tonic, subdominant and dominant note.

7. (a)   What is the relative major of A minor? _____

   (b)   What is the tonic note of A minor?   _____

   (c)   What is the key signature of A minor? _____

   (d)   Which degree of the scale do you raise in A minor Harmonic? _____

   (e)   What is the dominant note of A minor? _____

   (f)   Which two notes do you raise in the ascending scale of A minor melodic? _____

   (g)   What do the two notes in (f) become? _____

   (h)   What accidentals do you use in the descending scale of A minor melodic? _____

   (i)   What is the subdominant note of A minor? _____

MINOR SCALES THAT HAVE SHARPS.

THE SCALE OF E MINOR.

The relative major of E minor is G major because
   1. I to III is E to G
   2. Three semitones up from E is G♮.

So the key signature of E minor is the same as that of G major: 1 sharp.

The tonic of E minor is E. The subdominant of E minor is A. The dominant of E minor is B.

To write the scale of E minor harmonic with a key signature —
1. Write the notes from E up to E and down again.
2. Add the key signature.
3. Raise the seventh note D one semitone by adding a sharp to make it D♯ both ascending and descending.

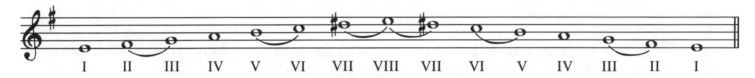

To write the scale of E minor harmonic without a key signature —
1. Write the notes from E up to E and down again.
2. Put a sharp in front of each F because this sharp occurs in the key signature.
3. Raise the seventh note D one semitone by adding a sharp to make it D♯ both ascending and descending.

To write the scale of E minor melodic with a key signature —
1. Write the notes from E up to E and down again.
2. Add the key signature.
3. Ascending: raise the sixth note C and the seventh note D one semitone by adding a sharp to each.
   Descending: lower the same two notes one semitone by adding a natural to each.

To write the scale of E minor melodic without a key signature —
1. Write the notes from E up to E and down again.
2. Put a sharp in front of each F because this sharp occurs in the key signature.
3. Ascending: raise the sixth note C and the seventh note D one semitone by adding a sharp to each.
   Descending: lower the same two notes one semitone by adding a natural to each.

I   II   III   IV   V   VI   VII   VIII   VII   VI   V   IV   III   II   I

EXERCISES

1. Add the correct key signature and accidentals to make the scale of E minor harmonic.

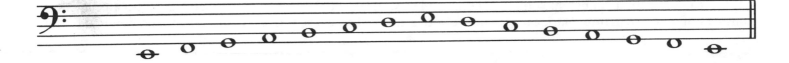

2. Add the correct key signature and accidentals to make the scale of E minor melodic.

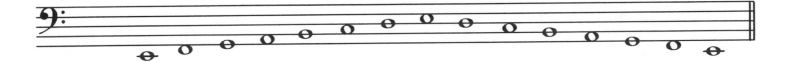

3. Without using a key signature add accidentals to make the scale of E minor harmonic.

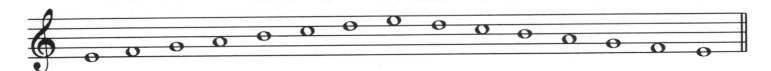

4. Without using a key signature add accidentals to make the scale of E minor melodic.

5. Write the scale of E minor harmonic ascending only in the treble clef in quarter notes, using the correct key signature. Mark each semitone with a slur and label each tonic note.

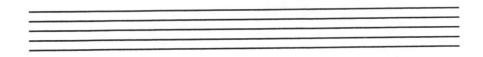

96

6. Write the scale of E minor melodic ascending and descending in the bass clef in whole notes. Mark each semitone with a slur and label each   dominant note.

7. Write the scale of E minor harmonic descending only in the bass clef in half notes, using accidentals instead of a key signature. Mark each semitone with a slur and label the subdominant note.

8. Write the scale of E minor melodic ascending and descending in the treble clef in half notes using accidentals instead of a key signature. Mark each semitone with a slur and label each tonic, subdominant and dominant note.

For extra practice:

THE SCALE OF B MINOR

The relative major of B minor is D major because

    1. I to III is B to D
    2. Three semitones up from B is D♮.

So the key signature of B minor is the same as that of D major: 2 sharps.

The tonic of B minor is B. The dominant of B minor is F♯. The subdominant of B minor is E.

To write the scale of B minor harmonic with a key signature —
1. Write the notes from B up to B and down again.
2. Add the key signature.
3. Raise the seventh note A one semitone by adding a sharp to make it A♯ both ascending and descending.

To write the scale of B minor harmonic without a key signature —
1. Write the notes from B up to B and down again.
2. Put a sharp in front of each F and each C because these sharps occur in the key signature.
3. Raise the seventh note A one semitone by adding a sharp to make it A♯ both ascending and descending.

To write the scale of B minor melodic with a key signature —
1. Write the notes from B up to B and down again.
2. Add the key signature.
3. Ascending: raise the sixth note G and the seventh note A one semitone by adding a sharp to each.
   Descending: lower the same two notes one semitone by adding a natural to each.

98

To write the scale of B minor melodic without a key signature —
1. Write the notes from B up to B and down again.
2. Put a sharp in front of each F and each C because these sharps occur in the key signature.
3. Ascending: raise the sixth note G and the seventh note A one semitone by adding a sharp to each.
   Descending: lower the same two notes one semitone by adding a natural to each.

I   II   III   IV   V   VI   VII   VIII   VII   VI   V   IV   III   II   I

EXERCISES

1. Add the correct accidentals instead of using a key signature to make the scale of B minor melodic.

2. Add the correct key signature and accidentals to make the scale of B minor harmonic.

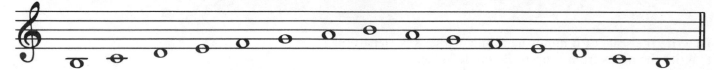

3. Write the scale of B minor harmonic descending only in the bass clef in eighth notes using accidentals instead of a key signature. Mark each semitone with a slur and label each tonic note.

4. Write the scale of B minor melodic ascending and descending in the treble clef in half notes using the correct key signature. Mark each semitone with a slur and label each subdominant note.

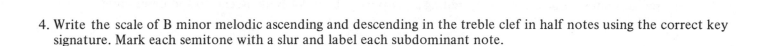

5. Write the scale of B minor melodic ascending only in the bass clef in whole notes using accidentals instead of a key signature.

6. Write the scale of B minor harmonic ascending and descending in the bass clef in half notes, using the correct key signature.

7. Write the scale of B minor melodic descending only in the bass clef in quarter notes using the correct key signature.

THE SCALE OF F♯ MINOR.

The relative major of F♯ minor is A major because

    1. I to III is F♯ to A
    2. Three semitones up from F♯ is A♮.

So the key signature of F♯ minor is the same as that of A major: 3 sharps.

The tonic of F♯ minor is F♯. The dominant of F♯ minor is C♯. The subdominant of F♯ minor is B.

To write the scale of F♯ minor harmonic with a key signature —
1. Write the notes form F up to F and down again.
2. Add the key signature.
3. Raise the seventh note E one semitone by adding a sharp to make it E♯ both ascending and descending.

To write the scale of F♯ minor harmonic without a key signature —
1. Write the notes from F up to F and down again.
2. Put a sharp in front of each F, each C and each G because these sharps occur in the key signature.
3. Raise the seventh note E one semitone by adding a sharp to make it E♯ both ascending and descending.

To write the scale of F♯ minor melodic with a key signature —
1. Write the notes from F up to F and down again.
2. Add the key signature.
3. Ascending: raise the sixth note D and the seventh note E one semitone by adding a sharp to each.
    Descending: lower the same two notes one semitone by adding a natural to each.

To write the scale of F♯ minor melodic without a key signature —
1. Write the notes from F up to F and down again.
2. Put a sharp in front of each F, each C and each G because these sharps occur in the key signature.
3. Ascending: raise the sixth note D and the seventh note E one semitone by adding a sharp to each.
    Descending: lower the same two notes one semitone by adding a natural to each.

100

EXERCISES

1. Write the scale of F♯ minor harmonic ascending in the bass clef in half notes using the correct key signature. Mark each semitone with a slur and label the dominant note.

2. Write the scale of F♯ minor harmonic descending in the treble clef in whole notes using accidentals only. Mark each semitone with a slur and label the subdominant note.

3. Write the scale of F♯ minor melodic ascending and descending in the bass clef in quarter notes using the correct key signature. Mark each semitone with a slur and label each tonic and dominant note.

4. Write the scale of F♯ minor melodic ascending and descending in the treble clef in whole notes using accidentals instead of a key signature. Mark each semitone with a slur and label each subdominant note.

5. Write the scale of F♯ minor harmonic descending only in the bass clef in eighth notes, using accidentals instead of a key signature.

6. Write the scale of F♯ minor harmonic descending only in the bass clef in whole notes, using the correct key signature.

THE SCALE OF C# MINOR.

The relative major of C# minor is E major because

    1. I to III is C# to E.
    2. Three semitones up from C# is E♮.

So the key signature of C# minor is the same as that of E major: 4 sharps.

The tonic of C# minor is C# . The dominant of C# minor is G# . The subdominant of C# minor is F# .

To write the scale of C# minor harmonic with a key signature —
1. Write the notes from C up to C and down again.
2. Add the key signature.
3. Raise the seventh note B one semitone by adding a sharp to make it B# both ascending and descending.

To write the scale of C# minor harmonic without a key signature —
1. Write the notes from C up to C and down again.
2. Put a sharp in front of each F, each C, each G and each D because these sharps occur in the key signature.
3. Raise the seventh note B one semitone by adding a sharp to make it B# both ascending and descending.

To write the scale of C# minor melodic with a key signature —
1. Write the notes from C up to C and down again.
2. Add the key signature.
3. Ascending: raise the sixth note A and the seventh note B one semitone by adding a sharp to each.
   Descending: lower the same two notes one semitone by adding a natural to each.

To write the scale of C# minor melodic without a key signature —
1. Write the notes from C up to C and down again.
2. Put a sharp in front of each F, each C, each G, and each D because these sharps occur in the key signature.
3. Ascending: raise the sixth note A and the seventh note B one semitone by adding a sharp to each.
   Descending: lower the same two notes one semitone by adding a natural to each.

EXERCISES

1. Add accidentals to make the scale of C♯ minor harmonic.

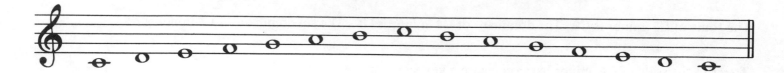

2. Add accidentals to make the scale of C♯ minor melodic.

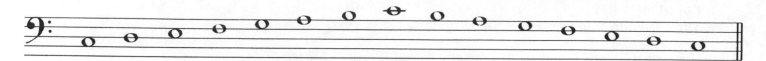

3. Write the scale of C♯ minor harmonic ascending in the treble clef in half notes, using the correct key signature. Mark each semitone with a slur and label the dominant note.

4. Write the scale of C♯ minor harmonic descending in the bass clef in sixteenth notes using accidentals only. Mark each semitone with a slur and label the subdominant note.

5. Write the scale of C♯ minor melodic ascending and descending in the bass clef in quarter notes using accidentals instead of a key signature. Mark each semitone with a slur and label each tonic and subdominant note.

6. Write the scale of C♯ minor melodic ascending and descending in the treble clef in whole notes, using the correct key signature. Mark each semitone with a slur and label each tonic, subdominant and dominant note.

REVIEW EXERCISES FOR MINOR SCALES THAT HAVE SHARPS

1. Add the correct clef, key signature and accidentals to make these scales.

C# minor harmonic

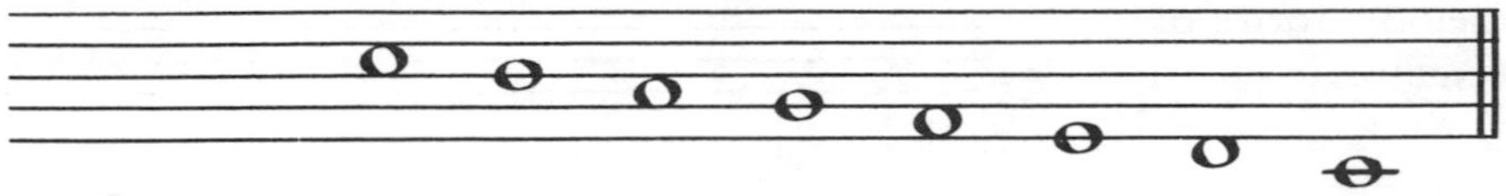

A minor melodic

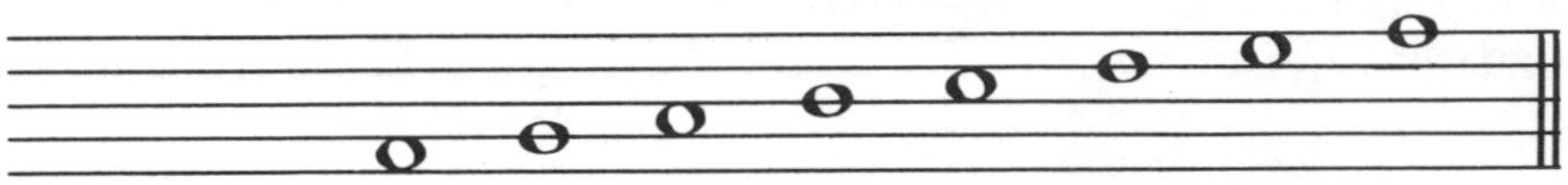

B minor melodic

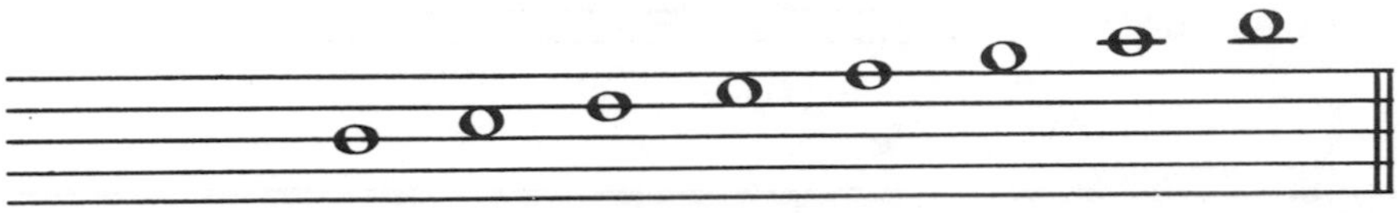

F# minor harmonic

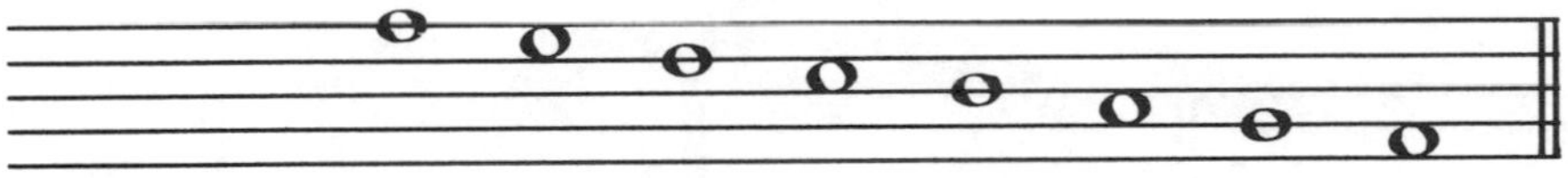

E minor melodic

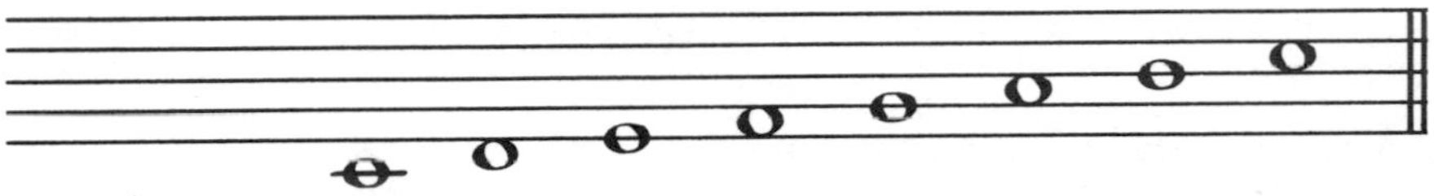

2. Write these scales in the bass clef ascending in half notes, using the correct key signature for each.

The relative minor, harmonic form, of D major.

B minor melodic.

The relative major of C# minor.

The harmonic minor scale that has a key signature of 1 sharp.

F♯ minor melodic.

The relative minor, melodic form, of C major.

The melodic minor scale that has a key signature of 4 sharps.

The relative major of F♯ minor.

3. For each key write the key signature and the subdominant note.

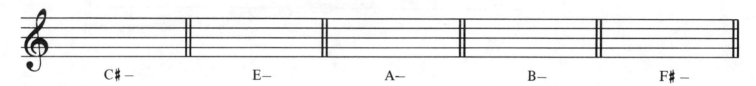

C♯ —   E—   A—   B—   F♯ —

4. For each key write the key signature and the dominant note.

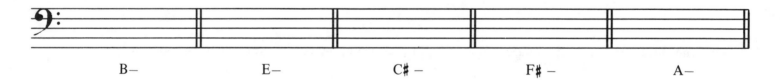

B—   E—   C♯ —   F♯ —   A—

Instead of using the word "major" the plus sign + is frequently used as an abbreviation.

Instead of the word "minor" the minus sign - is frequently used as an abbreviation, as in the exercise above.

Here are examples of the minor scales that have more than four sharps, which you will learn later.

G♯ minor has 5 sharps:

harmonic:

melodic:

D♯ minor has 6 sharps:
harmonic:

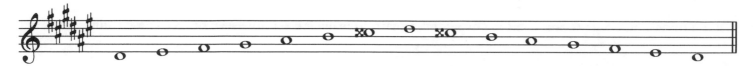

melodic:

A♯ minor has 7 sharps:
harmonic:

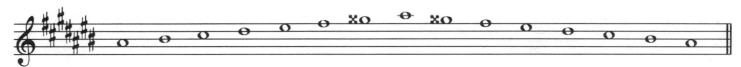

melodic:

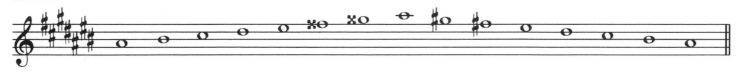

Here is a complete list of all the sharp minor scales.

E minor has 1 sharp: F♯

B minor has 2 sharps: F♯ C♯

F♯ minor has 3 sharps: F♯ C♯ G♯

C♯ minor has 4 sharps: F♯ C♯ G♯ D♯

G♯ minor has 5 sharps: F♯ C♯ G♯ D♯ A♯

D♯ minor has 6 sharps: F♯ C♯ G♯ D♯ A♯ E♯

A♯ minor has 7 sharps: F♯ C♯ G♯ D♯ A♯ E♯ B♯

MINOR SCALES THAT HAVE FLATS.

THE SCALE OF D MINOR.

The relative major of D minor is F major because
    1. I to III is D to F.
    2. Three semitones up from D is F♮.

So the key signature of D minor is the same as that of F major: 1 flat.

The tonic of D minor is D. The dominant of D minor is A. The subdominant of D minor is G.

To write the scale of D minor harmonic with a key signature —
1. Write the notes from D up to D and down again.
2. Add the key signature.
3. Raise the seventh note C one semitone by adding a sharp to make it C♯ both ascending and descending.

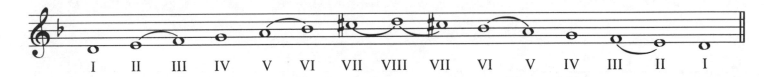

To write the scale of D minor harmonic without a key signature —
1. Write the notes from D up to D and down again.
2. Put a flat in front of each B because this flat occurs in the key signature.
3. Raise the seventh note C one semitone by adding a sharp to make it C♯ both ascending and descending.

To write the scale of D minor melodic with a key signature —
1. Write the notes from D up to D and down again.
2. Add the key signature.
3. Ascending: raise the sixth note B♭ one semitone by adding a natural, and the seventh note C one semitone by adding a sharp.
    Descending: lower the seventh note C♯ by adding a natural and the sixth note B♮ one semitone by adding a flat.

To write the scale of D minor melodic with a key signature —

1. Write the notes from D up to D and down again.
2. Put a flat in front of each B, because this flat occurs in the key signature.
3. Ascending: raise the sixth note B♭ one semitone by adding a natural and the seventh note C one semitone by adding a sharp.
   Descending: lower the seventh note one semitone by adding a natural, and the sixth note one semitone by adding a flat.

NOTE: In the ascending scale the flat and the natural in front of the B cancel each other and therefore are not necessary. So what you really should do to raise the B♭ is simply erase the flat sign. The note then becomes B as there is no key signature, and the scale will look like this:

EXERCISES

1. Add accidentals to make the scale of D minor harmonic.

2. Add a key signature and accidentals to make the scale of D minor melodic.

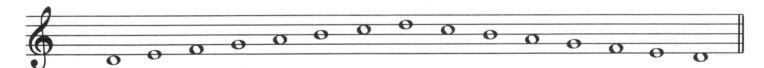

3. Add accidentals only to make the scale of D minor melodic.

4. Write the scale of D minor harmonic ascending in the treble clef in whole notes, using the correct key signature. Mark each semitone with a slur and label the dominant note.

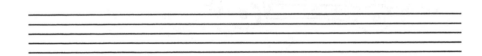

5. Write the scale of D minor harmonic descending in the bass clef in quarter notes, using accidentals instead of a key signature.

6. Write the scale of D minor melodic ascending in the treble clef in half notes using accidentals only. Mark each semitone with a slur and label the subdominant note.

7. Write the scale of D minor melodic descending in the treble clef in eighth notes using accidentals only. Mark each semitone with a slur and label each tonic note.

8. Write the scale of D minor harmonic ascending and descending in the bass clef in whole notes using the correct key signature.

9. Write the scale of D minor melodic in the treble clef in quarter notes ascending and descending using the correct key signature.

THE SCALE OF G MINOR.

The relative major of G minor is B♭ major because

  1. I to III is G to B
  2. Three semitones up from G is B♭.

So the key signature of G minor is the same as that of B♭ major: 2 flats.

The tonic of G minor is G. The dominant of G minor is D. The subdominant of G minor is C.

To write the scale of G minor harmonic with a key signature —
1. Write the notes from G up to G and down again.
2. Add the key signature.
3. Raise the seventh note F one semitone by adding a sharp to make it F♯ both ascending and descending.

To write the scale of G minor harmonic without a key signature —
1. Write the notes from G up to G and down again.
2. Put a flat in front of each B and each E because these flats occur in the key signature.
3. Raise the seventh note F one semitone by adding a sharp to make it F♯ both ascending and descending.

To write the scale of G minor melodic with a key signature —
1. Write the notes from G up to G and down again.
2. Add the key signature.
3. Ascending: raise the sixth note E one semitone by adding a natural, and the seventh note F one semitone by adding a sharp.
   Descending: lower the seventh note F♯ by adding a natural and the sixth note E by adding a flat.

To write the scale of G minor melodic without a key signature —
1. Write the notes from G up to G and down again.
2. Put a flat in front of each B and each E because these flats occur in the key signature.
3. Ascending: raise the sixth note E♭ one semitone by removing the flat, and the seventh note F one semitone by adding a sharp.
   Descending: lower the seventh note F♯ by adding a natural, and the sixth note E by adding a flat.

EXERCISES

1. Write the scale of G minor harmonic ascending and descending in the treble clef in half notes using the correct key signature. Mark each semitone with a slur and label each tonic, subdominant and dominant note.

2. Write the scale of G minor harmonic ascending and descending in the bass clef in eighth notes using accidentals instead of a key signature. Mark each semitone with a slur and label each tonic, subdominant and dominant note.

3. Write the scale of G minor melodic ascending and descending in the bass clef in whole notes, using the correct key signature. Mark each semitone with a slur and label each tonic note.

4. Write the scale of G minor melodic ascending and descending in the treble clef in sixteenth notes using accidentals instead of a key signature. Mark each semitone with a slur and label each subdominant and dominant note.

5. Write the scale of G minor harmonic descending in the treble clef in whole notes using accidentals only.

6. Write the scale of G minor melodic descending only in the bass clef in quarter notes, using the correct key signature.

THE SCALE OF C MINOR.

The relative major of C minor is E♭ major because

1. I to III is C to E
2. Three semitones up from C is E♭.

So the key signature of C minor is the same as that of E♭ major: 3 flats.

The tonic of C minor is C. The dominant of C minor is G. The subdominant of C minor is F.

To write the scale of C minor harmonic with a key signature —
1. Write the notes from C up to C and down again.
2. Add the key signature.
3. Raise the seventh note B♭ one semitone by adding a natural to make it B♮ both ascending and descending.

To write the scale of C minor harmonic without a key signature —
1. Write the notes from C up to C and down again.
2. Put a flat in front of each B, each E and each A because these flats occur in the key signature.
3. Raise the seventh note B♭ one semitone by removing the flat to make it B♮ both ascending and descending.

To write the scale of C minor melodic with a key signature —
1. Write the notes from C up to C and down again.
2. Add the key signature.
3. Ascending: raise the sixth note A♭ and the seventh note B♭ one semitone by adding a natural to each.
   Descending: lower the same notes by adding a flat to each.

To write the scale of C minor melodic without a key signature —
1. Write the notes from C up to C and down again.
2. Put a flat in front of each B, each E and each A because these flats occur in the key signature.
3. Ascending: raise the sixth note A♭ and the seventh note B♭ one semitone by removing the flat in front of each.
   Descending: lower the same two notes one semitone by adding a flat to each.

EXERCISES

1. Add the correct accidentals to make the scale of C minor melodic.

2. Add the correct key signature and accidentals to make the scale of C minor harmonic.

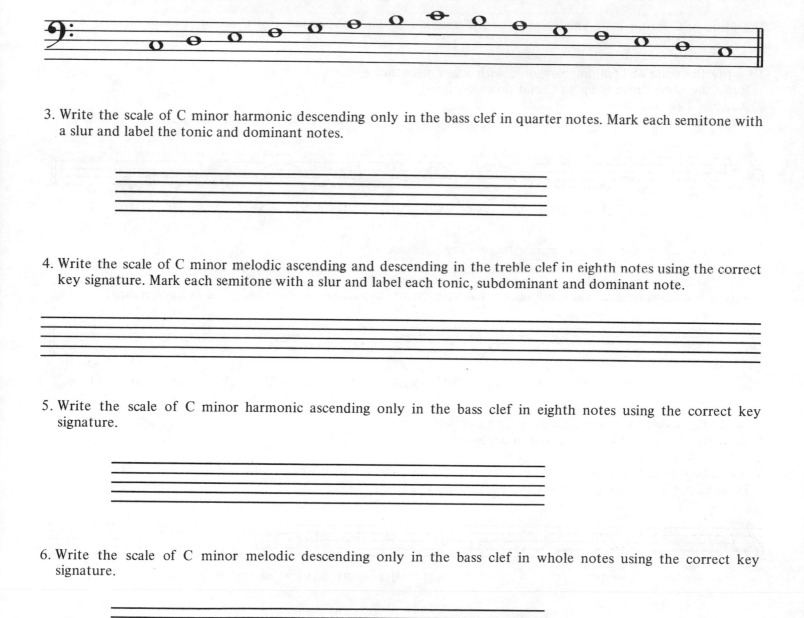

3. Write the scale of C minor harmonic descending only in the bass clef in quarter notes. Mark each semitone with a slur and label the tonic and dominant notes.

4. Write the scale of C minor melodic ascending and descending in the treble clef in eighth notes using the correct key signature. Mark each semitone with a slur and label each tonic, subdominant and dominant note.

5. Write the scale of C minor harmonic ascending only in the bass clef in eighth notes using the correct key signature.

6. Write the scale of C minor melodic descending only in the bass clef in whole notes using the correct key signature.

7. Write the scale of C minor melodic ascending only in the bass clef in half notes using accidentals instead of a key signature.

THE SCALE OF F MINOR.

The relative major of F minor is A♭ major because

   1. I to III is F to A
   2. Three semitones up from F is A♭.

So the key signature of F minor is the same as that of A♭ major: 4 flats.

The tonic of F minor is F. The dominant of F minor is C. The subdominant of F minor is B♭.

To write the scale of F minor harmonic with a key signature –
1. Write the notes from F up to F and down again.
2. Add the key signature.
3. Raise the seventh note E♭ one semitone by adding a natural to make it E♮ both ascending and descending.

To write the scale of F minor harmonic without a key signature –
1. Write the notes from F up to F and down again.
2. Put a flat in front of each B, each E, each A and each D because these flats occur in the key signature.
3. Raise the seventh note E♭ one semitone by removing the flat to make it E♮ both ascending and descending.

To write the scale of F minor melodic with a key signature –
1. Write the notes from F up to F and down again.
2. Add the key signature.
3. Ascending: raise the sixth note D♭ and the seventh note E♭ one semitone by adding a natural to each.
   Descending: lower the same two notes by adding a flat to each.

To write the scale of F minor melodic without key signature –
1. Write the notes from F up to F and down again.
2. Put a flat in front of each B, each E, each A and each D because these flats occur in the key signature.
3. Ascending: raise the sixth note D♭ and the seventh note E♭ one semitone by removing the flat in front of each.
   Descending: lower the same two notes one semitone by adding a flat to each.

114

EXERCISES

1. Add the correct key signature and accidentals to make the scale of F minor harmonic.

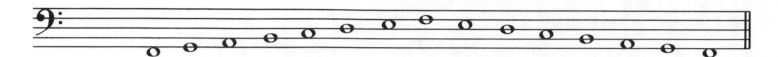

2. Add the correct key signature and accidentals to make the scale of F minor melodic.

3. Add accidentals to make the scale of F minor harmonic.

4. Add accidentals to make the scale of F minor melodic.

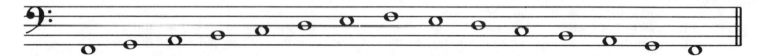

5. Write the scale of F minor harmonic ascending only in the treble clef in half notes using the correct key signature. Mark each semitone with a slur and label the dominant note.

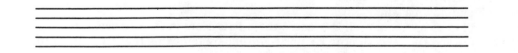

6. Write the scale of F minor melodic ascending and descending in the bass clef in quarter notes. Mark each semitone with a slur and label each subdominant note.

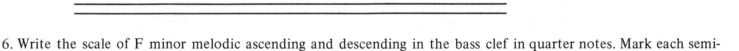

7. Write the scale of F minor harmonic descending only in the bass clef in whole notes using accidentals instead of a key signature. Mark each semitone with a slur and label each tonic note.

8. Write the scale of F minor melodic ascending and descending in the treble clef in eighth notes using accidentals instead of a key signature. Mark each semitone with a slur and label each tonic, subdominant and dominant note.

REVIEW EXERCISES FOR MINOR SCALES THAT HAVE FLATS

1. For each key write the key signature and the tonic note.

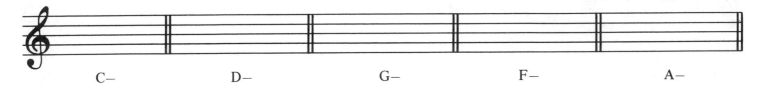

G—   F—   C—   A—   D—

2. For each key write the key signature and the dominant note.

C—   D—   G—   F—   A—

3. Write these scales in the bass clef ascending only in half notes using accidentals instead of a key signature.

The tonic minor (harmonic)
of D major.

The harmonic minor scale
whose key signature is
two flats.

The relative minor
(melodic) of E♭ major.

The melodic minor
scale whose dominant
is C.

116

Here are examples of the minor scales that have more than four flats, which you will learn later.

B♭ minor has 5 flats:

harmonic:

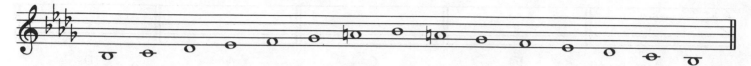

melodic:

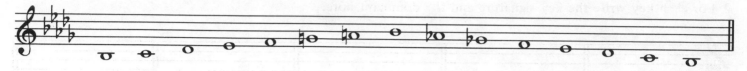

E♭ minor has 6 flats:

harmonic:

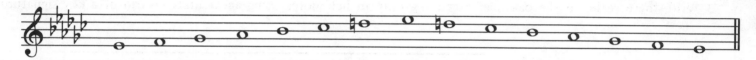

melodic:

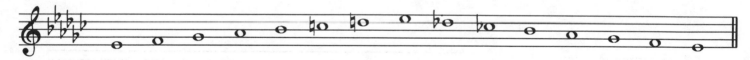

A♭ minor has 7 flats:

harmonic:

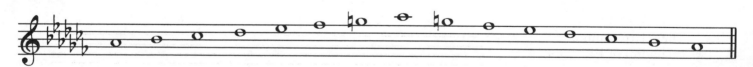

melodic:

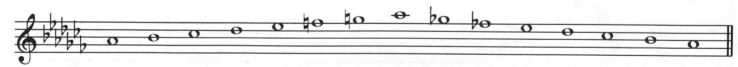

Here is a complete list of all the flat minor scales.

D minor has 1 flat: B♭

G minor has 2 flats: B♭ E♭

C minor has 3 flats: B♭ E♭ A♭

F minor has 4 flats: B♭ E♭ A♭ D♭

B♭ minor has 5 flats: B♭ E♭ A♭ D♭ G♭

E♭ minor has 6 flats: B♭ E♭ A♭ D♭ G♭ C♭

A♭ minor has 7 flats: B♭ E♭ A♭ D♭ G♭ C♭ F♭

TABLE OF RELATIVE MAJOR AND MINOR KEYS

?

1. This minor key has two sharps, and the seventh note is A sharp. What is the key? _____

2. This minor key's seventh note is F sharp. What is its name? _____

3. The third flat of this minor key is A flat. The seventh note is E♮. What is the key? _____

4. This minor key has four sharps. What is the name of the seventh note? _____

5. This minor key's seventh note is D sharp. What is the name of the key? _____

6. The seventh note of this minor key is G sharp. How many sharps or flats are in the key signature? _____

7. The dominant of this minor key is D. What is its key signature? _____

8. The tonic of this minor key is F sharp. What is the dominant? _____

9. This minor key has two sharps. What is the name of its dominant? _____

10. This minor key has one flat less than F minor. What is the name of its seventh note? _____

REVIEW EXERCISES FOR ALL MAJOR AND MINOR SCALES.

1. (a)　Write the scale of A major ascending in the bass clef using the correct key signature.

(b)　Write its relative minor harmonic descending in the treble clef using accidentals instead of a key signature.

(c)　Write its tonic minor melodic ascending in the bass clef.

2. (a)　Write the scale of G minor harmonic ascending in the treble clef using the correct key signature.

(b)　Write its tonic major descending in the bass clef using the correct key signature.

(c)　Write its relative major descending in the bass clef using accidentals instead of a key signature.

120

3. (a) Write the scale of F major descending in the bass clef using accidentals instead of a key signature.

   (b) Write its tonic minor (harmonic) ascending in the treble clef using the correct key signature.

   (c) Write its relative minor (melodic) ascending in the bass clef using the correct key signature.

4. Add the correct clef, key signature and accidentals where necessary to form these scales:

   (a) A minor harmonic.

   (b) A♭ major.

   (c) D major.

   (d) G minor melodic.

   (e) A major.

   (f) B minor harmonic.

(g) C♯ minor melodic.

(h) C minor melodic.

(i) B♭ major.

(j) D minor harmonic.

5. Add the correct clef, key signature and accidentals where necessary to form these scales:

(a) F♯ minor melodic.

(b) E minor harmonic.

(c) G major.

(d) D minor melodic.

(e) F major.

(f) C minor harmonic.

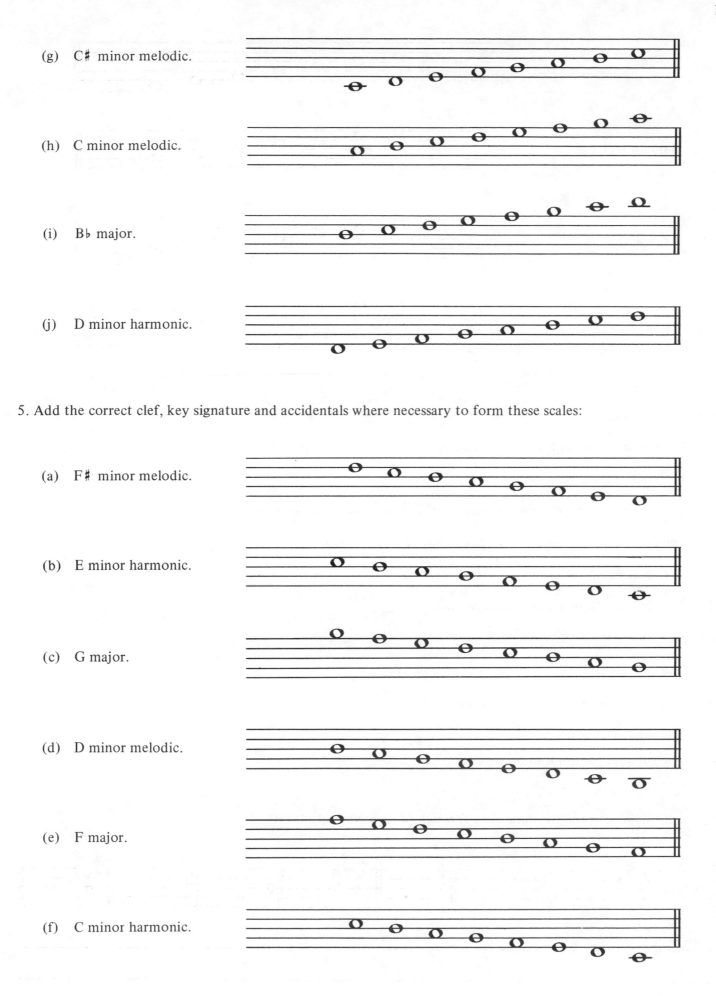

122

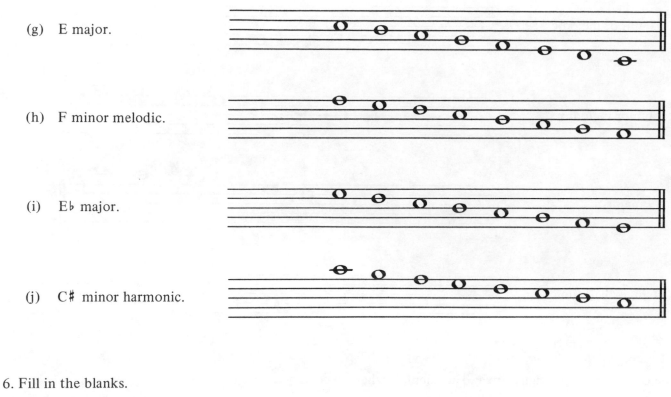

(g) E major.

(h) F minor melodic.

(i) E♭ major.

(j) C♯ minor harmonic.

6. Fill in the blanks.

(a) The key signature of E major is _____

(b) The relative minor of C major is _____

(c) The minor key that has a key signature of 2 flats is _____

(d) The dominant of F minor is _____

(e) The tonic major of E minor is _____

(f) The tonic of A♭ major is _____

(g) E♭ major is the relative major of _____

(h) The key signature of F♯ minor is _____

(i) The dominant of G minor is _____

(j) The tonic of A major is _____

(k) The subdominant of C minor is _____

7. Name the major key and the minor key for each of these key signatures:

E♭ + _____ _____ _____ _____ _____ _____ _____ _____

C- _____ _____ _____ _____ _____ _____ _____ _____

CHAPTER 4

ITALIAN TERMS.

WORDS THAT REFER TO TEMPO or TIME

SLOW — grave — extremely slow and solemn
adagio — very slow
lento — slow
largo — slow and broad
larghetto — less slow than largo

MEDIUM — andante — rather slow, at a moderate walking pace
andantino — a little faster than andante
moderato — moderate pace
allegretto — fairly quick, a little slower than allegro

FAST — con moto — with movement
allegro — lively, rather quick
vivace — quick and lively
veloce — with velocity
rapido — rapidly
presto — very quick
prestissimo — as quick as possible

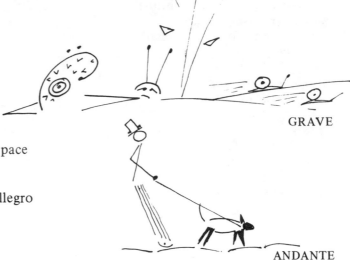

GRAVE

ANDANTE

PRESTO

WORDS THAT REFER TO CHANGES IN TEMPO

accelerando — gradually getting quicker
meno mosso — less movement, slower
piu mosso — more movement, faster
rallentando (rall) — gradually getting slower
ritardando (rit) — gradually getting slower
tempo giusto — in strict time
tempo rubato — robbed time

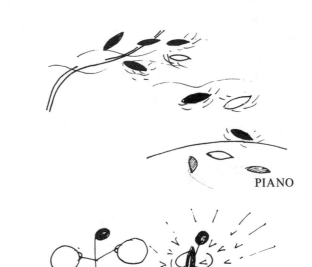

PIANO

WORDS THAT REFER TO VOLUME

ppp -piano possible — as soft as possible

pp -pianissimo — very soft

p -piano — soft

mp -mezzopiano — slightly louder than piano

mf -mezzoforte — slightly softer than forte

f -forte — loud

ff -fortissimo — very loud

fff -forte possible — as loud as possible

FORTE

WORDS THAT REFER TO CHANGES IN VOLUME

crescendo-cresc. — ————— gradually louder
decrescendo-decresc. —
diminuendo-dim. — ————— gradually softer
sforzando- *sfz* or *sf* — strongly accented
forte-piano- *fp* — loud then suddenly soft
rinforzando — strengthening the tone

CRESCENDO

WORDS THAT REFER TO STYLE IN PLAYING

alla marcia — in the style of a march
arpeggio — the notes of a chord played one after the other instead of all at the same time
brillante or con brio — with brilliance
cantabile — in a singing style
con forza — with force or strength
dolce — sweetly
furioso — furiously
giocoso — gay, playful
grazioso — graceful
legato — smoothly
maestoso — majestically
marcato — emphasized
scherzando — playfully
staccato — detached
tenuto — held
vivace — lively

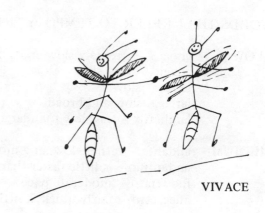

VIVACE

SIGNS AND ABBREVIATIONS.

ACCENTS

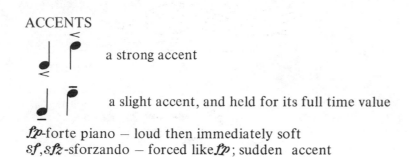

a strong accent

a slight accent, and held for its full time value

fp-forte piano — loud then immediately soft
sf,sfz-sforzando — forced like *fp*; sudden accent

REPEATS

repeat the previous section from   or from the beginning.

| 1st | 2nd |

the passage is to be repeated, but with the ending changed the second time

D.C. — da capo — repeat from the beginning
fine — often used after D.C. to indicate where the end is
D.S.-dal segno — repeat from the sign

DEGREES OF STACCATO

staccato — the note is held for about half its value, like this

staccatissimo — very short, held for about a quarter of its value, like this

mezzo staccato — slightly detached, like this

If a group of notes is to be played mezzo staccato, a slur is used with the dots.

DIFFERENT FORMS OF

A TIE — joins two notes of the same pitch.

A SLUR — joins two or more notes of different pitch. On the piano all the notes within the slur are to be played legato.

OTHERS

⌢ fermata — a pause. The note or rest is to be held longer than its normal value.

M.D. - mano destra — right hand
M.S. - mano sinestra — left hand

8va — when above the notes, play them an octave higher
   — when below the notes, play them an actave lower

con 8 - - - - - - - -⌐ play the notes in octaves

M.M.-Maelzel's Metronome. An instrument used for beating time.

Ped - - - - - - - - -* Put down the damper pedal at 'ped' and let it up at *

una corda — use the soft pedal

con ped. con pedale — with the pedal

tr 〰〰〰〰 — play a trill

126

EXERCISES

1. Draw a line from each word or sign in the first column to the one in the second column that means the OPPOSITE.

accelerando

meno mosso   crescendo

                                             forte

staccato   piu mosso

diminuendo   ritardando

piano   legato

2. Put these abbreviations in order from softest to loudest.

mp   *f*   *ppp*   *ff*   *p*   *mf*   *pp*   *fff*

___ ___ ___ ___ ___ ___ ___ ___

3. Put these words in order from slowest to quickest.

adagio   moderato   presto   lento   allegro

___ ___ ___ ___ ___

4. Draw a line from each word in the first column to the word in the second column that means the same.

lento   presto

rapido   diminuendo

descrescendo

rall.   rit.

                                             largo

5. Unscramble these words.

tagole (smoothly) _____   unetto (held) _____

gadoia (very slow) _____   trofe   (loud) _____

nolte   (slowly) _____   garlo   (slowly)_____

petom   (time) _____   ipodar (rapidly)_____

coled   (sweetly) _____   nife   (the end)_____

AN EASY PUZZLE

ACROSS

3. legato

6.  𝆑

7. ♮

DOWN

1. Presto

2. lento

4. ⌢

5. ♭

128

A MORE DIFFICULT PUZZLE

ACROSS

1. Time.
8. Measure.
9. In a singing style
10. Joins 2 notes of the same pitch
11. Loud.
13. Sweetly.
16. with
17. the end.
19. not.
20. Smoothly.
22. Quickly.
23. Gradually slower.
26. Very quickly.
28. 'fine'.
29. A member of the string family.
30. Slow down.
31. _____ corda pedal.
32. An accidental.
33. The fifth note.

DOWN

1. Key note.
2. Soft.
3. less
4. Treble or Bass.
5. F clef
6. Getting softer.
7. It is oval, not round.
9. Getting louder.
12. An instrument used in Church.
14. Slowly.
15. Harmonic or Melodic _____
17. Loud.
18. a phrase mark.
21. Playfully.
24. Held.
25. Right hand.
26. Very soft.
27. an accidental.

CHAPTER 5

INTERVALS

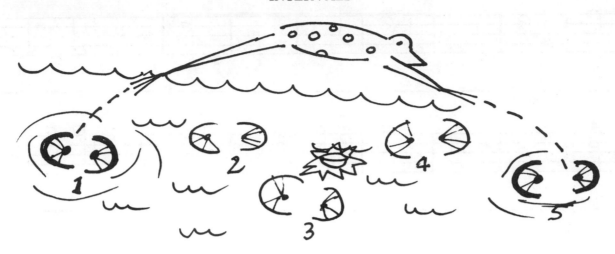

An INTERVAL is the distance in pitch between any two notes.

If the notes are played at the same time it is an HARMONIC interval.

If the notes are played one after the other it is a MELODIC interval.

To find the size of an interval count the number of letter names including both the bottom and the top notes.

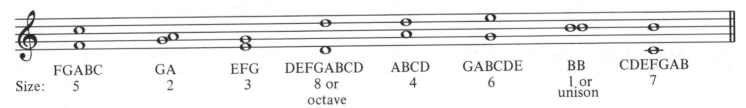

	FGABC	GA	EFG	DEFGABCD	ABCD	GABCDE	BB	CDEFGAB
Size:	5	2	3	8 or octave	4	6	1 or unison	7

EXERCISES

1. Name the size of each of these harmonic intervals:

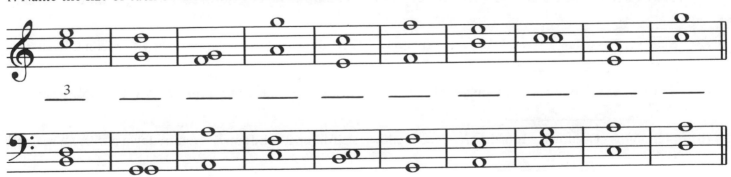

3

2. Name the size of each of these melodic intervals.

3. Write an interval the right size above these notes.

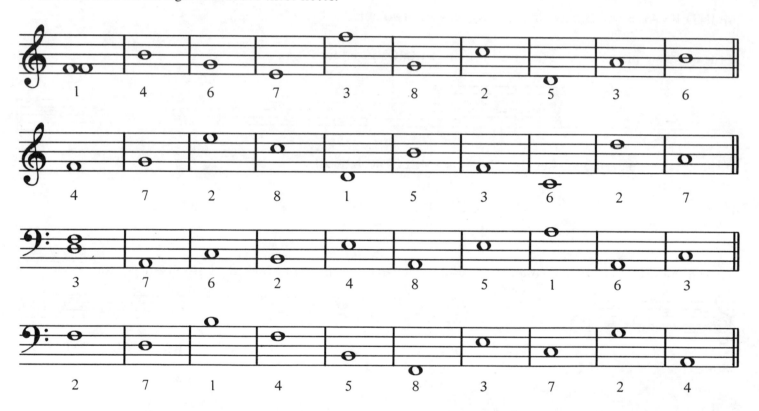

4. Name the last note of each question.

(a) Start on A. Go up a sixth; down a second; down a third; up an octave; down a fourth; up a third. What note is it? _____

(b) Start on F. Go up a second; up a fourth; down a fifth; down a third; up a sixth; down a second. What note is it? _____

(c) Start on C. Go down a third; up a fifth; up a sixth; down a second; down a fourth; down a third. What note is it? _____

(d) Start on G. Go down a fourth; up a second; down a fifth; up a third; up a seventh; down a third. What note is it? _____

(e) Start on E. Go up a third; down a fifth; down a third; up a fourth; down a second; down a sixth What note is it? _____

What word do these answers spell? _____

Intervals are always named as if the bottom note were the tonic.

The intervals in a major key have the following names:

perfect unison or first	major second	major third	perfect fourth	perfect fifth	major sixth	major seventh	perfect octave

Here are the intervals above C in the scale of C major, with their correct names. **Play them and learn their sound.**

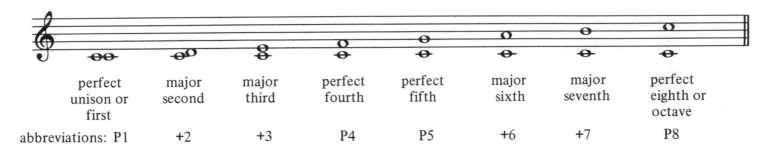

	perfect unison or first	major second	major third	perfect fourth	perfect fifth	major sixth	major seventh	perfect eighth or octave
abbreviations:	P1	+2	+3	P4	P5	+6	+7	P8

Here are the intervals above D in the scale of D major.

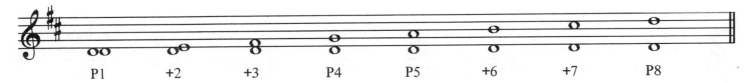

P1	+2	+3	P4	P5	+6	+7	P8

Here are the intervals above F in the scale of F major.

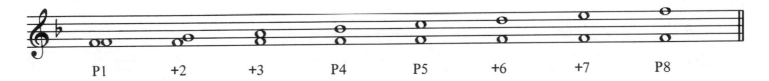

P1	+2	+3	P4	P5	+6	+7	P8

Notice that unisons, fourths, fifths and octaves are called PERFECT, and seconds, thirds, sixths and sevenths are called MAJOR.
The two on the outside and the two in the middle are the perfect ones, the others are major.

Remember when you name an interval to think of the bottom note as being the tonic.

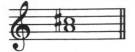
key: A major
letter names: ABC
size: 3

—The lower note is A. In the scale of A major, C♯ is its third note, so the interval is a major third (+3)

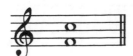
key: F major
letter names: FGABC
size: 5

—The lower note is F. In the scale of F major, C is the fifth note, so the interval is a perfect fifth (P5)

key: E major
letter   names: EF
size: 2

—The lower note is E. In the scale of E major, F♯ is its second note, so the interval is a major second (+2)

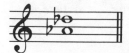

key: Ab major
letter names: ABCD
size: 4

—The lower note is A♭. In the scale of A♭ major, D♭ is its fourth note, so the interval is a perfect fourth (P4)

key: G major
letter names: GABCDEF
size: 7

—The lower note is G. In the scale of G major, F♯ is its seventh note, so the interval is a major seventh (+7)

EXERCISES

1. Here are all the intervals above E♭ in the key of E♭ major. Name each one.

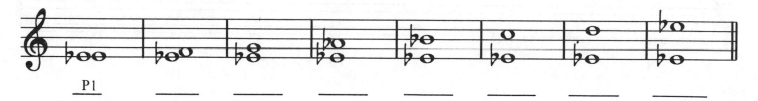

2. For each of these keys write the ascending scale using accidentals and then write the intervals above the tonic.

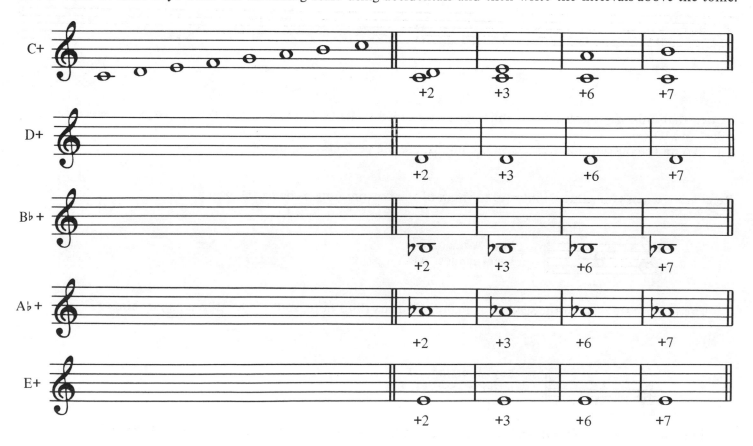

3. For each of these keys write the ascending scale using accidentals and then write the intervals above the tonic.

Eb+

+2   +3   +6   +7

G+

+2   +3   +6   +7

F+

+2   +3   +6   +7

A+

+2   +3   +6   +7

4. Name these harmonic intervals.

+3

134

5. Name these melodic intervals.

+7

6. For each key write the ascending scale using accidentals and then write the intervals above the tonic.

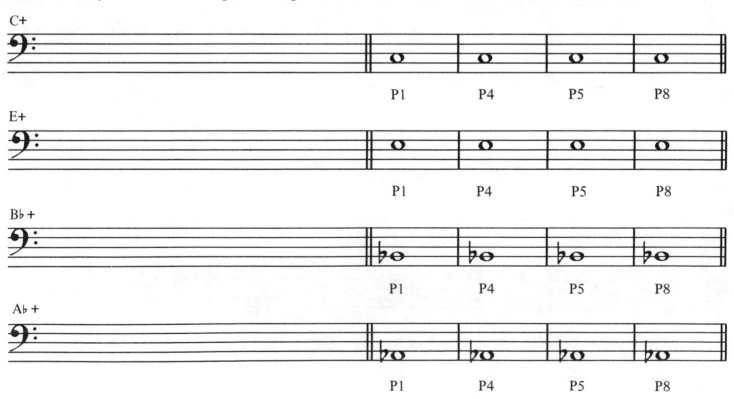

C+

P1   P4   P5   P8

E+

P1   P4   P5   P8

Bb +

P1   P4   P5   P8

Ab +

P1   P4   P5   P8

7. For each key write ascending scale using accidentals and then write the intervals above the tonic.

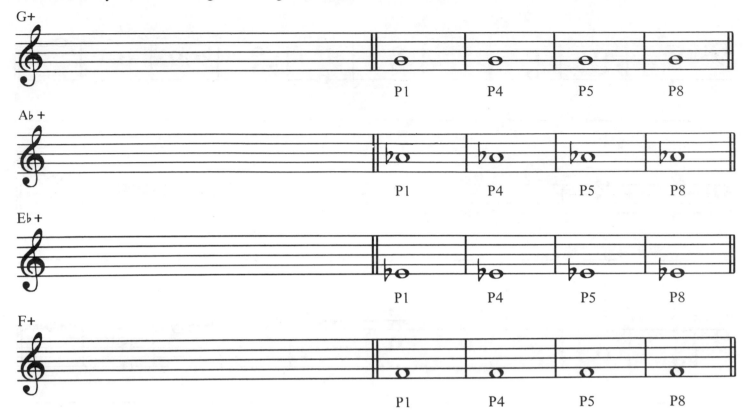

8. Name these intervals

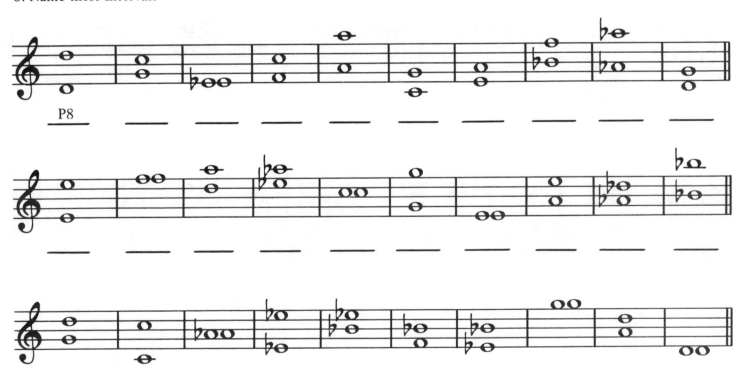

136

9. Name these intervals

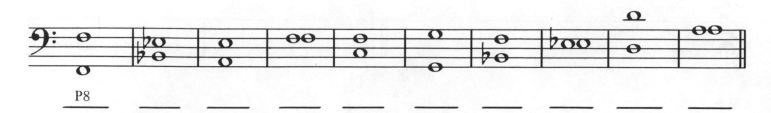

P8 _____ _____ _____ _____ _____ _____ _____ _____

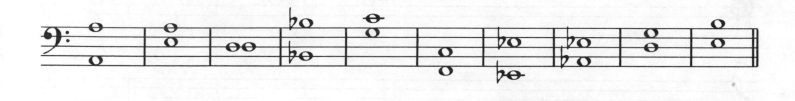

_____ _____ _____ _____ _____ _____ _____ _____ _____

_____ _____ _____ _____ _____ _____ _____ _____

10. Are the following intervals major or perfect?

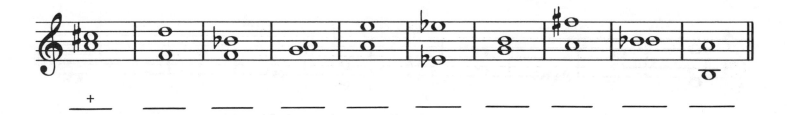

+ _____ _____ _____ _____ _____ _____ _____

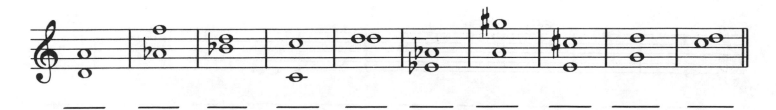

_____ _____ _____ _____ _____ _____ _____ _____

11. Name these intervals.

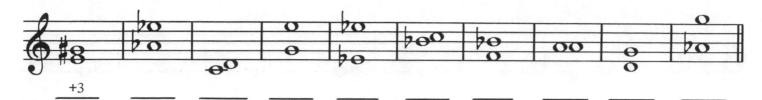

+3

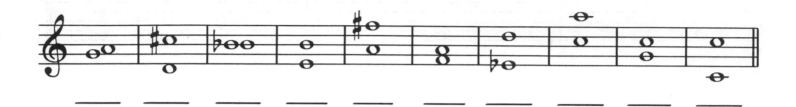

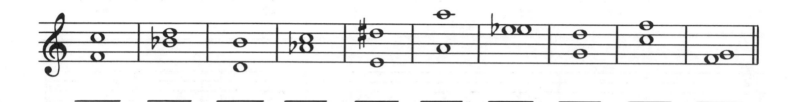

12.   Name these intervals

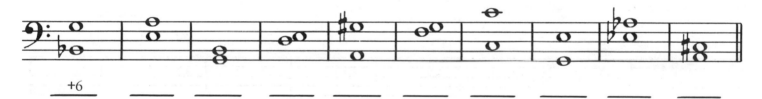

+6

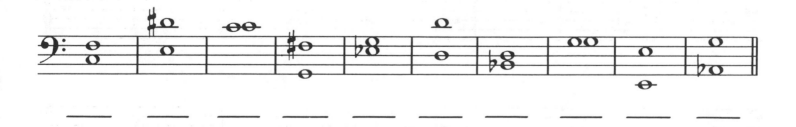

138

13. Write ALL of these as harmonic intervals above EACH given note.

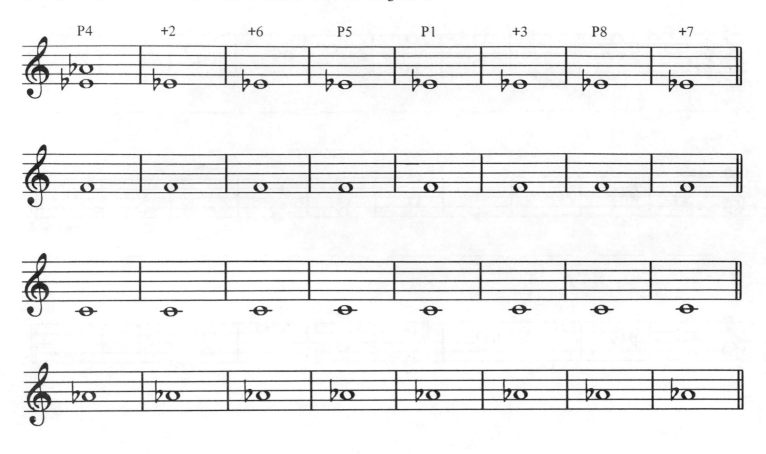

14. Write ALL of these as melodic intervals above EACH of these notes.

If any major interval is made one semitone smaller it becomes a MINOR interval.

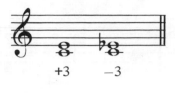

C to E is a major third.
C to E♭ is one semitone smaller so it is a minor third (−3)

E to F♯ is a major second.
E to F is one semitone smaller so it is a minor second (−2)

A to G♯ is a major seventh.
A to G is one semitone smaller so it is a minor seventh (−7)

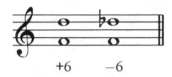

F to D is a major sixth.
F to D♭ is one semitone smaller so it is a minor sixth (−6)

In each of the above examples the upper note was lowered one semitone to make the major interval minor.

A major interval may also become minor if the lower note is *raised* one semitone.

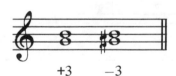

G to B is a major third.
G♯ to B is one semitone smaller so it is a minor third.

C to D is a major second.
C♯ to D is one semitone smaller so it is a minor second.

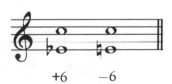

E♭ to C is a major sixth.
E to C is one semitone smaller so it is a minor sixth.

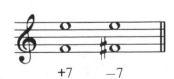

F to E is a major seventh.
F♯ to E is one semitone smaller so it is a minor seventh.

EXERCISES

1. Change these major intervals into minor intervals by adding an accidental to the top note.

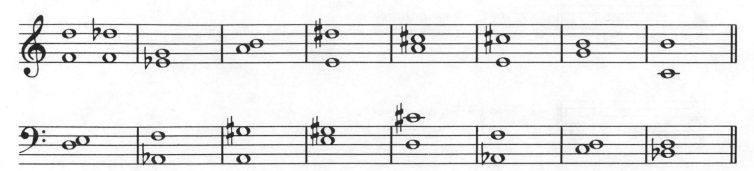

2. Change these minor intervals into major intervals by adding an accidental to the top note.

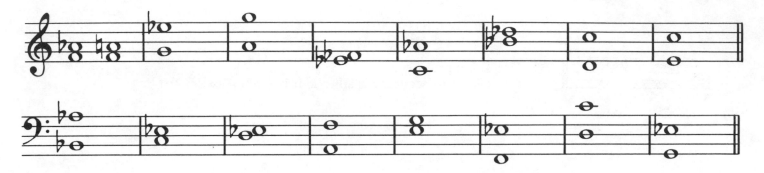

3. Are the following intervals major or minor?

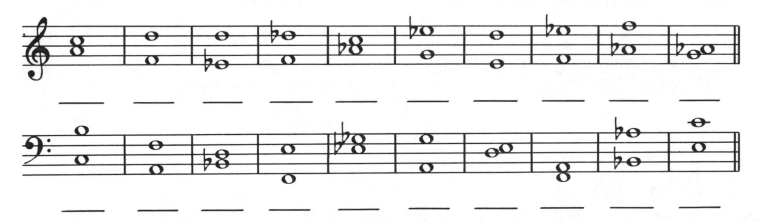

4. Change these major intervals into minor intervals by adding an accidental to the top note.

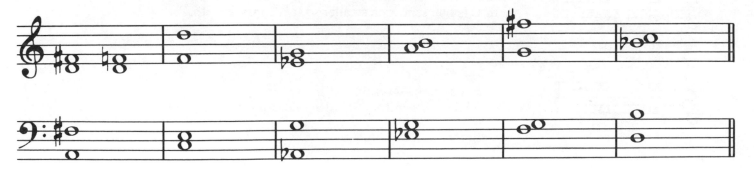

5. Change these minor intervals into major intervals by adding an accidental to the bottom note.

6. Name these intervals.

7. Name these intervals.

8. Write ALL of these as melodic intervals above EACH given note.

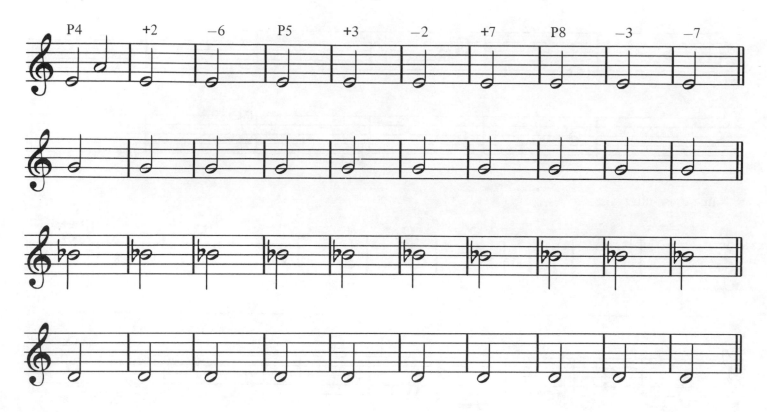

9. Write ALL of these as harmonic intervals above EACH of these notes.

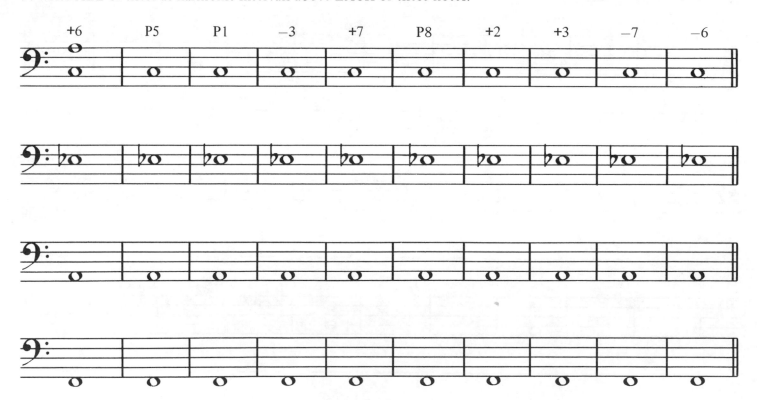

10. Name these harmonic intervals.

P4 _____ _____ _____ _____ _____ _____ _____

11. Name these melodic intervals.

P4 _____ _____ _____ _____ _____ _____ _____

HOW MANY OF EACH MUSICAL SIGN CAN YOU FIND?

trills _____   flats _____

quarter notes _____   staccatos _____

sharps _____   bar lines _____

staves _____   sixteenth rests _____

pauses _____   crescendo signs _____

forte signs _____   half notes _____

whole notes _____   naturals _____

diminuendo signs _____   half rests _____

repeat signs _____   eighth rests _____

whole rests _____   quarter rests _____

slurs or ties _____   brackets _____

accents _____   sixteenth notes _____

bass clefs _____   treble clefs _____

bar lines _____   piano signs_____

CHAPTER 6

TRIADS.

If you play any note and play a third above it and a third above that, the three notes will form a TRIAD. A triad is any chord that has three different notes that are built up in this way. The note that the triad is built on — that is, the lowest note — is called the ROOT. The middle note is called the third and the top note is called the fifth because it is five notes above the root.

TRIADS IN MAJOR KEYS.

You can build a triad on any degree of a major scale. The three most important triads in any key are the ones built on the tonic, the subdominant and the dominant. Here are the triads on each degree of the scale of D major. The tonic, subdominant and dominant triads are marked.

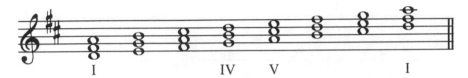

THE TONIC TRIAD

To build a TONIC triad start with the tonic as the root and add the third and the fifth notes of the scale.

Here is the tonic triad of C major:

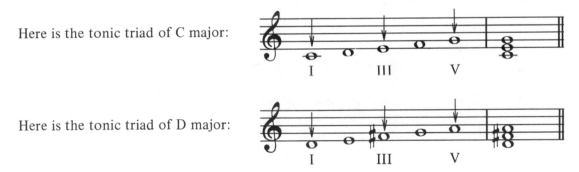

Here is the tonic triad of D major:

Here are some tonic triads in other major keys:

Each of these triads has a major third and a perfect fifth above its root. When a triad has these two intervals it is called a MAJOR triad. The tonic triad of every major key is a MAJOR triad.

THE DOMINANT TRIAD

To build a DOMINANT triad use the fifth (dominant) note of the scale as the root and add a third and a fifth above it according to the notes of the scale.

Here is the dominant triad of C major:

Here is the dominant triad of D major:

Here are some dominant triads in other major keys:

The dominant triad of every major key is a MAJOR triad since it has a major third and a perfect fifth above its root.

THE SUBDOMINANT TRIAD.

To build a SUBDOMINANT triad use the fourth (subdominant) note of the scale as the root and add a third and a fifth above it according to the notes of the scale.

Here is the subdominant triad of C major:

Here is the subdominant triad of D major:

Here are some subdominant triads in other major keys:

The subdominant triad of every major key is a MAJOR triad since it has a major third and a perfect fifth above its root.

147

EXERCISES

1. Write the tonic triad of each of these keys using the correct key signature for each.

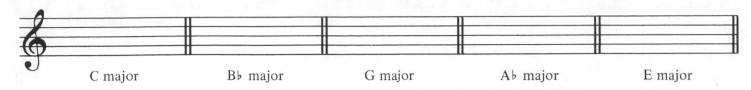

C major · · · · · · B♭ major · · · · · · G major · · · · · · A♭ major · · · · · · E major

2. Write the tonic triad of each of these keys using accidentals instead of a key signature.

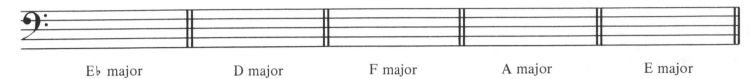

E♭ major · · · · · · D major · · · · · · F major · · · · · · A major · · · · · · E major

3. Write the dominant triad of each of these keys using the correct key signature for each.

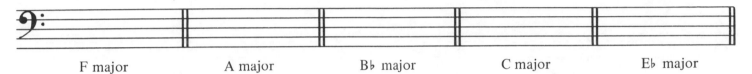

F major · · · · · · A major · · · · · · B♭ major · · · · · · C major · · · · · · E♭ major

4. Write the dominant triad of each of these keys using accidentals instead of a key signature.

D major · · · · · · G major · · · · · · E♭ major · · · · · · A♭ major · · · · · · E major

5. Write the subdominant triad of each of these keys using the correct key signature for each.

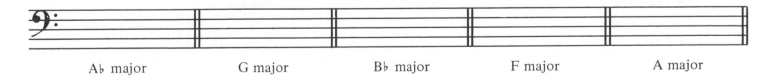

E♭ major · · · · · · F major · · · · · · D major · · · · · · E major · · · · · · C major

6. Write the subdominant triad of each of these keys using accidentals instead of a key signature.

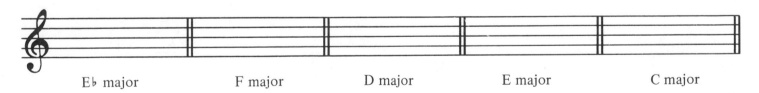

A♭ major · · · · · · G major · · · · · · B♭ major · · · · · · F major · · · · · · A major

7. Write a major triad using each of these notes as the root.

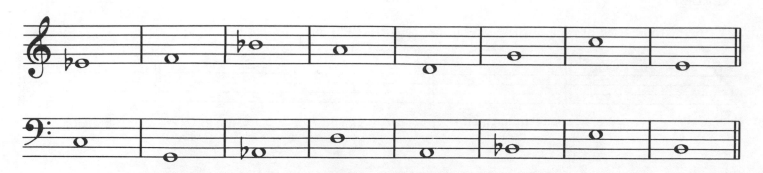

TRIADS IN MINOR KEYS.

As in the major keys you can build a triad on any degree of a minor scale. The harmonic form of the minor scale is used for building chords.

Here are the triads built on each degree of the scale of D minor harmonic. The tonic, subdominant and dominant triads are marked.

THE TONIC TRIAD

To build a TONIC TRIAD start with the tonic as the root and add the third and the fifth notes of the minor scale, just as you did in the major keys.

Here is the tonic triad of C minor

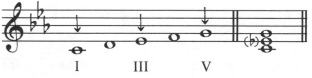

Here is the tonic triad of D minor:

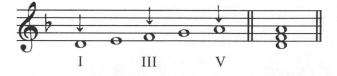

Here are some tonic triads in other minor keys.

Notice that each of these triads has a *minor* third and a perfect fifth above its root. When a triad has these two intervals it is called a MINOR TRIAD. The tonic triad of every minor key is a minor triad.

Play major and minor triads on the piano. Listen carefully to the difference in sound so that you learn to recognize them by ear.

THE DOMINANT TRIAD

To build the DOMINANT triad in a minor key use the fifth (dominant) note of the scale as the root and add a third and a fifth above it according to the notes of the harmonic minor scale.

Here is the dominant triad of C minor:

Here is the dominant triad of D minor:

Here are some dominant triads in other minor keys:

A minor   F minor   C# minor

Notice that in minor keys the middle note of the dominant triad is the seventh note of the harmonic minor scale and must be raised by an accidental.

The dominant triad of every minor key is a MAJOR triad since it has a major third and a perfect fifth above its root.

Notice also that the notes of the dominant triad sound exactly the same in the major and tonic minor keys.

 This could be the dominant triad of either G major or G minor. Since accidentals were used instead of a key signature, both triads look the same.

But if you use a key signature they will look different even though they sound the same.

 This is the dominant triad of G major.

 This is the dominant triad of G minor.

THE SUBDOMINANT TRIAD.

To build the SUBDOMINANT triad in a minor key use the fourth (subdominant) note of the scale as the root and add a third and a fifth above it according to the notes of the harmonic minor scale.

Here is the subdominant triad of C minor:

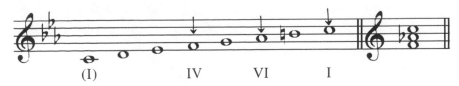

(I)   IV   VI   I

150

Here is the subdominant triad of D minor:

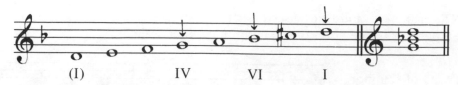

(I)   IV   VI   I

Here are some subdominant triads in other minor keys:

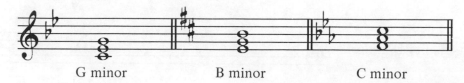

G minor   B minor   C minor

The subdominant triad of every minor key is a MINOR triad since it has a minor third and a perfect fifth above its root.

EXERCISES

1. Write the tonic triad of each of these keys using the correct key signature for each.

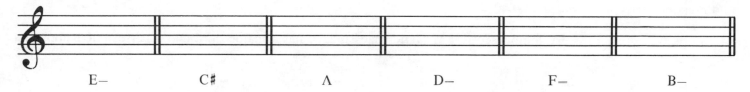

E–   C♯   A   D–   F–   B–

2. Write the tonic triad of each of these keys using accidentals instead of a key signature.

G–   B–   F♯–   C–   C♯–   F–

3. Write the dominant triad of each of these keys using the correct key signature for each.

G–   C♯–   F–   B–   D–   C–

4. Write the dominant triad of each of these keys using accidentals instead of a key signature.

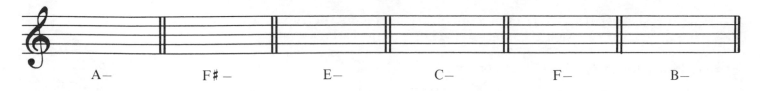

A–   F♯–   E–   C–   F–   B–

5. Write the subdominant triad of each of these keys using the correct key signature for each.

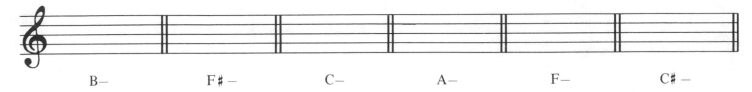

E–   C#–   G–   D–   F–   B–

6. Write the subdominant triad of each of these keys using accidentals instead of a key signature.

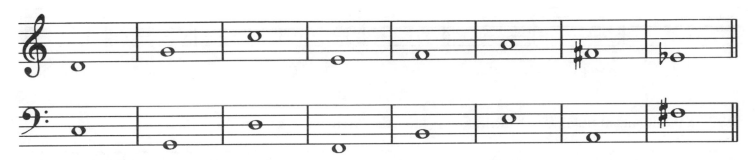

B–   F#–   C–   A–   F–   C#–

7. Write a minor triad using each of these notes as the root.

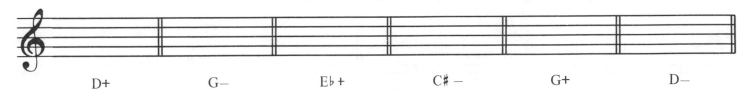

REVIEW EXERCISES

1. Write the tonic triad of each of these keys using the correct key signature for each.

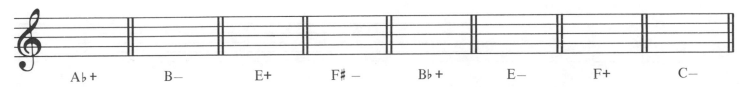

D+   G–   Eb+   C#–   G+   D–

2. Write the tonic triad of each of these keys using accidentals instead of a key signature.

Ab+   B–   E+   F#–   Bb+   E–   F+   C–

3. Write the tonic triad of each of these keys using the correct key signature for each.

B–   F#–   Bb+   D–   E+   Ab+

152

4. Write the tonic triad of each of these keys using accidentals instead of a key signature.

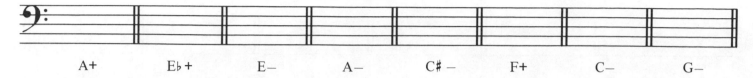

    A+   Eb+   E−   A−   C#−   F+   C−   G−

5. Write the dominant triad of each of these keys using the correct key signature for each.

    D+   C#−   Bb+   D−   A+   C−

6. Write the dominant triad of each of these keys using accidentals instead of a key signature.

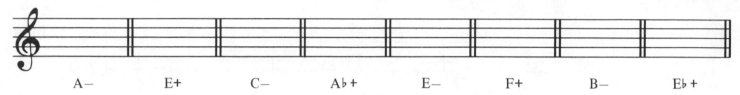

    A−   E+   C−   Ab+   E−   F+   B−   Eb+

7. Write the dominant triad of each of these keys using the correct key signature for each.

    C−   Eb+   C#−   A+   F+   G−

8. Write the dominant triad of each of these keys using accidentals instead of a key signature.

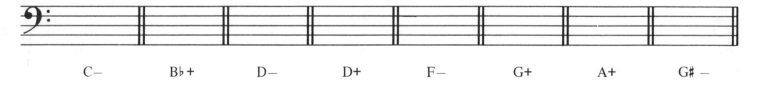

    C−   Bb+   D−   D+   F−   G+   A+   G#−

9. Write the subdominant triad of each of these keys using the correct key signature for each.

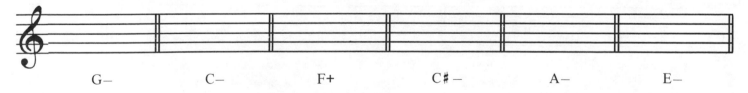

    G−   C−   F+   C#−   A−   E−

10. Write the subdominant triad of each of these keys using accidentals instead of a key signature.

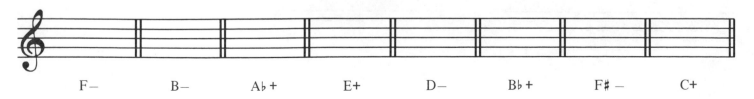

    F−   B−   Ab+   E+   D−   Bb+   F#−   C+

11. Write the subdominant triad of each of these keys using the correct key signature for each.

     C−   F+   E−   Bb+   F#−   E+

12. Write the subdominant triad of each of these keys using accidentals instead of a key signature.

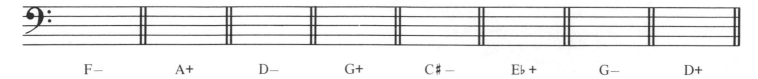

     F−   A+   D−   G+   C#−   Eb+   G−   D+

13. Name the key of each of these tonic triads.

14. Name the key of each of these dominant triads.

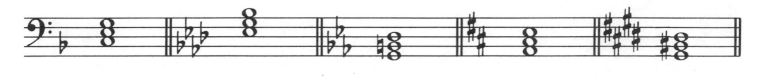

15. Name the key of each of these dominant triads.

16. Name the two keys of each of these dominant triads.

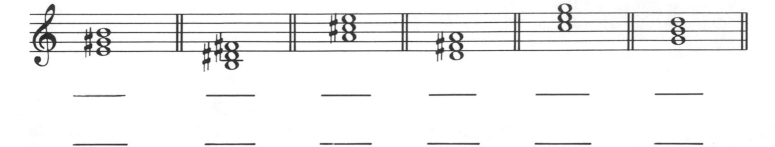

MORE EXERCISES. These questions are more difficult, but if you know your triads thoroughly you should be able to do them.

1. Are the following triads major or minor?

_____ _____ _____ _____ _____ _____ _____ _____ _____

2. Build a major triad using each of these notes as the root.

3. Build a minor triad using each of these notes as the root.

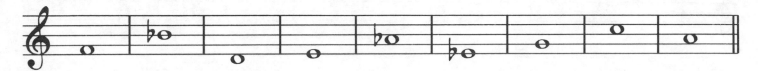

4. Name four keys in which each of these triads is found as either the tonic, the subdominant or the dominant triad.

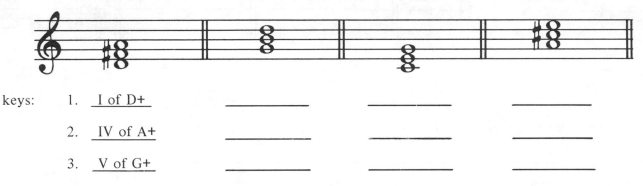

keys:	1.	I of D+	_____	_____	_____
	2.	IV of A+	_____	_____	_____
	3.	V of G+	_____	_____	_____
	4.	V of G−	_____	_____	_____

5. Write these triads in the treble clef.

(a) a major triad with F♯ as the third.
(b) a minor triad with B as the fifth.
(c) a major triad with E as the third.
(d) a minor triad with G as the fifth.
(e) a major triad with E♭ as the fifth.
(f) a minor triad with A♭ as the third.
(g) a minor triad with D as the third.
(h) a major triad with C as the fifth.

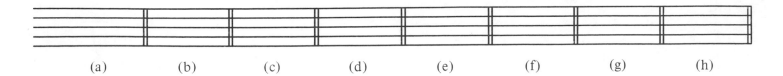

(a)　　　(b)　　　(c)　　　(d)　　　(e)　　　(f)　　　(g)　　　(h)

INTERVALS AND TRIADS

ACROSS

2. The subdominant triad of A minor.

4.  is a perfect _____ .

6. The note on which a triad is built.

11. The distance between any two notes.

13. The dominant triad of C major

14. The top two notes of the tonic triad of A minor.

15.  is a perfect _____ .

17. An interval contains _____ notes.

18. is a perfect _____ .

20. The tonic of F minor.

21. The fifth of the D major triad.

23. is a major _____ .

25. is a perfect _____ .

27. The third of the dominant triad of C major.

28. The subdominant triad of E minor.

DOWN

1. A chord with 3 notes built up in thirds.

3. The top note of a triad.

5. The fourth note of any scale is the _____ dominant.

7. The middle note of a triad.

8. is a _____ fifth.

9. is a _____ sixth.

10. is a major _____ .

12. are all _____ intervals.

16. One semitone smaller than major.

17. Every triad has _____ different notes.

19. The dominant triad of B flat major.

22. The tonic triad of D minor.

24. The subdominant triad of B minor.

26. A triad is built _____ from the root.

CHAPTER 7

SIMPLE TIME

Before you start this chapter review the section on time values in Chapter 1.

When you listen to music you hear a regular pattern of beats — some strong and some weak.

To show where the strong or accented beat comes there is a 'signpost' called a BAR LINE that is put before it. The distance between bar lines is called a BAR or MEASURE.

A DOUBLE BAR LINE is used at the end of a piece or at the end of a section of a piece.

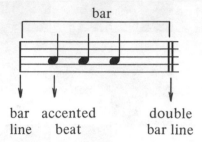

bar

bar   accented   double
line   beat   bar line

The number of beats in each bar will be the same throughout a piece.
A TIME SIGNATURE is placed at the beginning of a piece right after the key signature. This consists of two numbers, one on top of the other — example: 2
                                                                                                          4

The top number tells how many beats there will be in each bar.
The bottom number stands for the kind of note that is equal to one beat.

Here the time signature is 2/4. This is because the accent falls every second beat, and each beat equals a quarter note which is represented by the number 4.

accents: strong   weak   strong   weak   strong   weak   strong   weak
counts: 1   2   1   2   1   2   1   2

Whenever there are two beats in every bar it is called DUPLE TIME.

Here the time signature is 3/4. This is because the accent falls every third beat, and each beat equals a quarter note.

accents: strong   weak   weak   strong   weak   weak   strong   weak   weak
counts: 1   2   3   1   2   3   1   2   3

Whenever there are three beats in every bar it is called TRIPLE TIME.

Here the time signature is 4/4. This is because the accent falls every fourth beat, and each beat equals a quarter note.

accents: strong weak medium weak   strong weak medium weak
counts: 1   2   3   4   1   2   3   4

Whenever there are four beats in every bar it is called QUADRUPLE TIME.

Of course each beat can be divided into shorter notes or combined with other beats into longer notes but the total value of each beat will always be the same.

A bar can have notes, rests or a combination of both. Notice in the following example that all the notes belonging to one beat are grouped together so that you can see clearly where each beat begins.

counts 1 2 3 4   1 2 3 4   1 2 3 4   1 2 3 4 1   2   3   4   1 2 3 4

Look at any music and you will see that the time signature only appears once at the beginning. It is not repeated on every staff the way the key signature is.

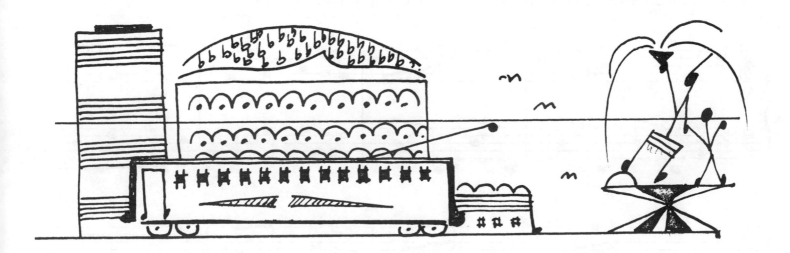

$\frac{2}{4}$ TIME

$\frac{2}{4}$ means $\frac{2}{\text{♩}}$ In other words in each bar there are two beats (a strong one and a weak one) and each beat adds up to a quarter note.

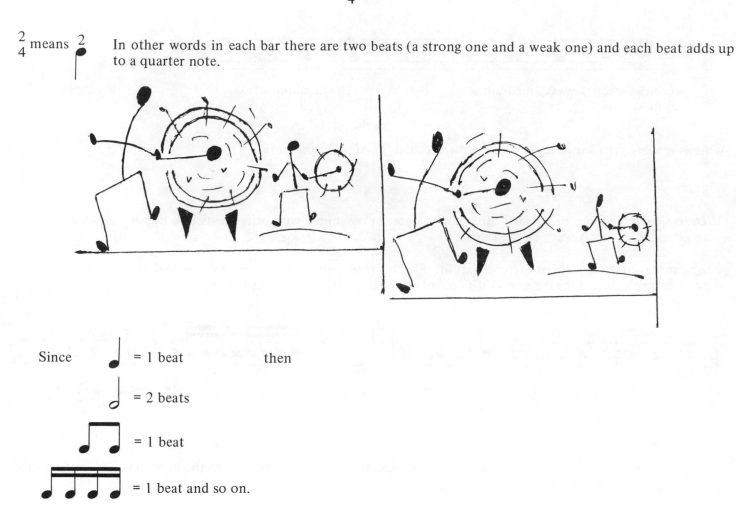

Since   ♩ = 1 beat   then

♩ ... = 2 beats

♫ = 1 beat

♬ = 1 beat and so on.

♩. = 1½ beats since ♩ = 1 and the dot = ♪ or ½ beat.

Have your teacher play this example from the Musette by Bach which is written in 2/4 time. Listen carefully and feel the accent every second beat. Do it several times, counting with your teacher.

EXERCISES

1. Count and clap this rhythm accenting the first beat of each bar.

2. Add counts to these bars.

3. Write 5 bars each with a different rhythm using half notes, quarter notes and eighth notes.

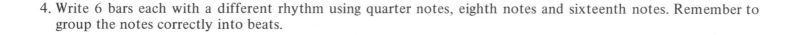

4. Write 6 bars each with a different rhythm using quarter notes, eighth notes and sixteenth notes. Remember to group the notes correctly into beats.

5. Add bar lines according to the time signature.

6. Add stems and group the notes correctly in 2/4 time.

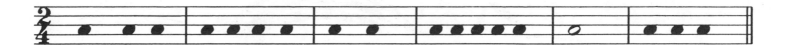

160

When there are rests in a bar they are put in so that you can see where each beat begins.

Notice in bar 5 two eighth rests are used instead of a quarter rest because each beat must be completed before the next beat begins.

In the last bar a whole rest is used. This is because whenever you have a whole bar's rest you use a whole rest. NO MATTER WHAT THE TIME SIGNATURE IS.

EXERCISES

Complete each bar with rests.

$\frac{3}{4}$ TIME

$\frac{3}{4}$ means $\frac{3}{\text{♩}}$ There are three beats in each bar (strong, weak, weak) and each beat adds up to a quarter note.

Have your teacher play this example from the Minuet in D minor by Bach, which is written in 3/4 time. Listen carefully and feel the accent every third beat. Do it several times, counting with your teacher.

EXERCISES

1. Count and clap this rhythm accenting the first beat of each bar.

162

2. Add counts to this rhythm.

3. Add one note in each bracket to complete the time of this rhythm.

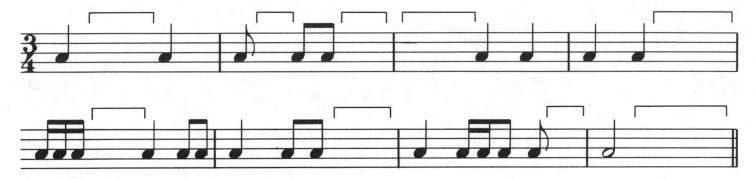

4. Add one rest in each bracket to complete the time of this rhythm.

5. Add bar lines according to the time signature

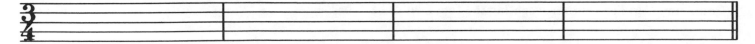

6. Add bar lines according to the time signature.

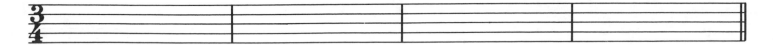

7. Write four bars, each with a different rhythm, using quarter notes, eighth notes and sixteenth notes. Remember to group the notes correctly into beats.

8. Write four bars, each with a different rhythm, using notes and rests.

$\frac{4}{4}$ TIME

$\frac{4}{4}$ means $\frac{4}{\text{♩}}$ There are four beats (strong, weak, medium, weak) in each bar and each beat adds up to a quarter note.

C is frequently used instead of 4/4 and stands for Common Time.

Have your teacher play this example from a Chorale by Bach, which is written in 4/4 time. Listen carefully and feel the accent every fourth beat. Do it several times counting with your teacher.

Whenever there are four beats in a bar it is usual to group together all the notes that belong to the first and second beats, and all the notes that belong to the third and fourth beats:

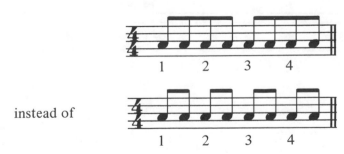

This grouping shows where the strong and medium accents are.

Similarly it is usual to use ONE rest for the first two beats and ONE rest for the last two beats in Quadruple time instead of using a separate rest for each beat.

1 2 3 4   1 2 3 4

However the second and third beats are never joined together.

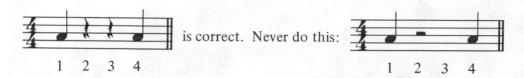

1 2 3 4   is correct. Never do this: 1 2 3 4

EXERCISES

1. Count and clap this rhythm putting a strong accent on each first beat and a medium accent on each third beat.

2. Add counts to this rhythm.

3. Add counts to this rhythm.

4. Add bar lines according to the time signature.

5. Write four bars of 4/4 time using a different combination of notes and rests in each bar.

6. Add rests to complete each bar.

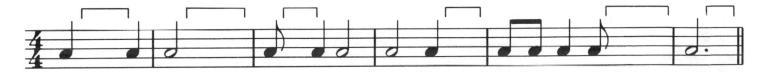

166

Here are three short pieces for you to sightread.

This one is in 2/4 and if you accent the first beat of each bar and play it very steadily it should sound like a march.

Here is the same tune written in 3/4. Now it should sound like a waltz.

Here is almost the same tune written in 4/4. Some notes have been added to the original tune. Can you hear which ones they are? Put a strong accent on the first beat of each bar and a slight accent on the third beat of each bar.

Not all tunes start on an accented beat.

When there is only part of a bar at the beginning, the number of beats in it is subtracted from the time in the last bar.

Notice that the number of beats in the first bar + the number of beats in the last bar adds up to one complete bar.

168

EXERCISES

1. Add counts to these rhythms.

2. Add the correct time signatures to these rhythms.

3. Add bar lines according to the time signature.

$$\frac{2}{2} \quad \frac{3}{2} \quad \text{and} \quad \frac{4}{2}$$

So far all the time signatures you have learned have had 4 as the bottom number — the quarter note equalled one beat.

There are also time signatures where a half note or an eighth note equals one beat.

When a HALF NOTE equals one beat instead of a quarter note it usually means that the beat is slower. The bottom number of the time signature will be 2.

2/2 means 2/♩ : 2 beats per bar, each beat adding up to a half note.

₵ is sometimes used instead of 2/2 and stands for 'cut time' or 'alla breve'.

3/2 means 3/♩ : 3 beats per bar, each beat adding up to a half note.

4/2 means 4/♩ : 4 beats per bar, each beat adding up to a half note.

Since ♩ = 1 beat, then 𝅝 = 2 beats

𝅝· = 3 beats

♩ = ½ beat

♫ = ½ beat and so on.

Look again at the Musette in 2/4 time on page 158.
This is how it looks written in 2/2 time — every note has twice the time value that it had before.

Study these examples carefully and notice the counting, the accents and how the notes and rests are grouped.

counts: 1   2   1   2   1   2   1   2
accents: s   w   s   w   s   w   s   (w)

counts: 2   1   2   1   2   1   2   1
accents: w   s   w   s   w   s   w   s

counts: 1   2   1   2   1   2   1   2   1   2
accents: s   (w)   s   (w)   s   w   s   (w)   (s)   (w)

counts: 1   2   3   1   2   3   1   2   3   1   2   3
accents: s w   w   s   w   w   s   w   w   s   (w w)

counts: 3   1   2   3   1   2   3   1   2   3   1   2
accents: w   s   w   w   (s)   w   w   s   w   w   s   (w)

counts: 1   2   3   1   2   3   1   2   3   1   2   3
accents: s (w) w   (s)   w   w   s   (w) w)   s   (w   w)

counts: 1   2   3   4   1 2 3 4   1   2   3   4   1   2   3   4
accents: s   w   m   w   s (w) m (w)   s   w   m   w   s   (w m w)

counts: 1   2   3   4   1   2   3   4   1   2   3   4
accents: s   w   m   w   (s) w   m   (w) s   (w   m   w)

counts: 4   1   2   3   4   1   2   3   4   1   2   3
accents: w   s   (w) m   w   s   w   m   w   s   (w   m)

Remember when adding rests that you must complete each beat before starting the next beat:

And complete each part of the beat before starting the next part:

As in 4/4 time the first two beats or the last two beats in 4/2 are given one rest instead of two.

Remember that a whole rest can equal two half rests as it did here, but it can also equal one whole bar's rest in any time signature (see page 160.)

A whole NOTE however ALWAYS equals two half notes.

EXERCISES

1. Add counts to these rhythms.

2. Write four bars, each with a different rhythm, using whole notes, half notes and quarter notes.

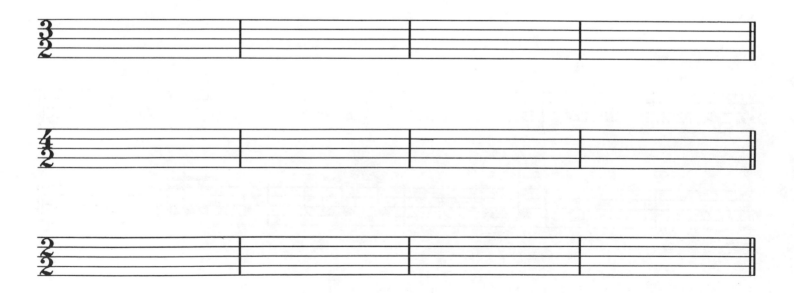

3. Write four bars each with a different rhythm using any note values you wish.

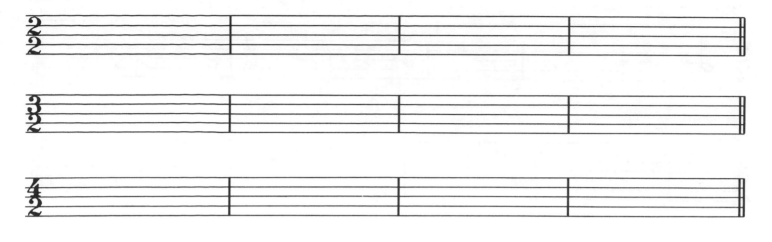

4. Write four bars each with a different rhythm using both notes and rests.

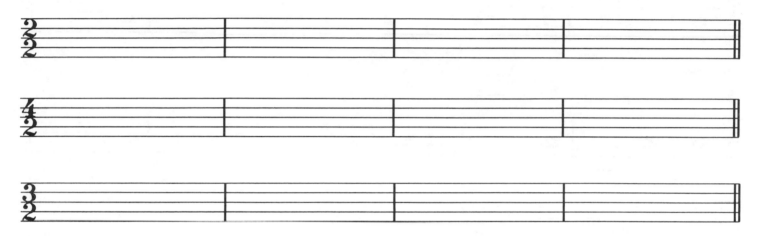

5. Add bar lines according to the time signature

174

6. Add rests to complete each of these bars.

$$\frac{2}{8} \quad \frac{3}{8} \quad \text{and} \quad \frac{4}{8}$$

When an EIGHTH note equals one beat it usually means that the beat is quite fast. The bottom number of the time signature will be 8.

$\frac{2}{8}$ means $\frac{2}{\eighthnote}$: 2 beats per bar, each beat adding up to an eighth note.

$\frac{3}{8}$ means $\frac{3}{\eighthnote}$: 3 beats per bar, each beat adding up to an eighth note.

$\frac{4}{8}$ means $\frac{4}{\eighthnote}$: 4 beats per bar, each beat adding up to an eighth note.

Since ♪ = 1

      then   ♩ = 2

            ♩. = 3

            ♬ = ½

            ♬ = 1 and so on.

Look again at the Minuet in 3/4 time on page 161.
This is how it looks written in 3/8 time — every note has half the time value that it had before.

Often in 2/8 and 3/8 all the notes in one bar are grouped together: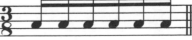

But this is still easier to read:

As in 4/4 and 4/2 the first two beats and the last two beats of 4/8 are given one rest

1 2 3 4   1 2 3 4

Study these examples carefully, noticing the grouping of notes and rests.

1   2   1   2   1   2   1   2   1   2

3   1 2 3   1   2   3   1   2   3   1   2   3   1   2

1 2 3 4   1 2 3 4   1 2 3 4   1   2 3 4   1 2 3 4   1 2 3 4

4   1   2   3   4   1 2 3 4   1   2   3   4   1   2   3   4   1 2 3

3   1 2 3 1 2 3 1   2   3   1 2 3   1 2 3   1 2 3   1 2 3 1 2 3 1 2

EXERCISES

1. Add counts to these rhythms.

2. Add bar lines according to the time signature

178

3. Write four bars each with a different rhythm using quarter notes, eighth notes and sixteenth notes.

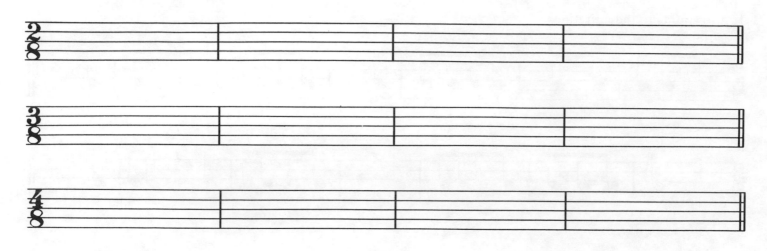

4. Write four bars, each with a different rhythm, using a combination of notes and rests.

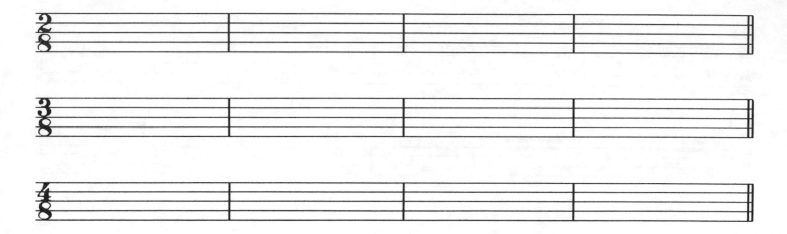

5. Add rests to complete each of these bars.

TRIPLETS

Sometimes in your music you will find  or ♩♩♩ or ♫♫

This is called a **TRIPLET** and the three notes are played in the time of two notes of the same value.

So ♫♫ = ♩♩ = ♩ and ♩♩♩ = ♩♩ = ♩ and ♫♫ = ♫♫ = ♪

Here is a part of a Minuet. Play it and see if you can play the triplets evenly and in time.

J. Haydn
(1732-1809)

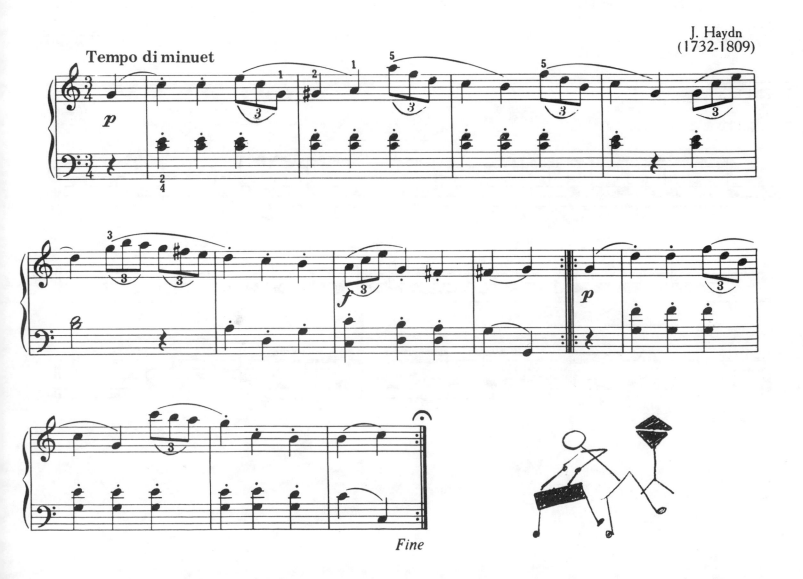

Tempo di minuet

Fine

If you have difficulty playing triplets it sometimes helps to say 'galloping' for ♩♩♩ and 'running' for ♫

Clap these rhythms and say the words.

say: running   running   galloping   running   galloping   running   galloping   running   running.
count: 1   2   3   1   2   3   1   2   3

say: walk   galloping   running   running   galloping   running   walk
count: 1   2   1   2   1   2   1   2

say: walk   galloping   walk   running   running   galloping   walk
count: 1   2   3   1   2   3   1   2   3

EXERCISES

1. Add counts to these bars.

2. Add the correct time signature to EACH of these bars.

3. Complete the following bars with rests.

4. Complete these bars by adding triplets.

182

REVIEW EXERCISES

1. Put the correct time signature at the beginning of EACH bar.

a.　　　　　b.　　　　　c.　　　　　d.　　　　　e.

f.　　　　　g.　　　　　h.　　　　　i.　　　　　j.

k.　　　　　l.　　　　　m.　　　　　n.

2. Complete the following bars with rests.

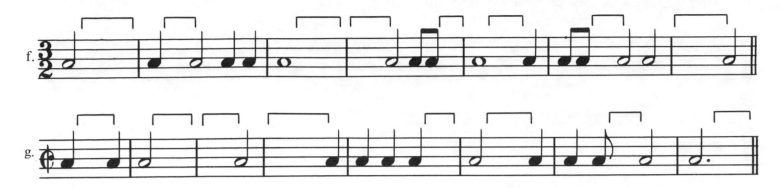

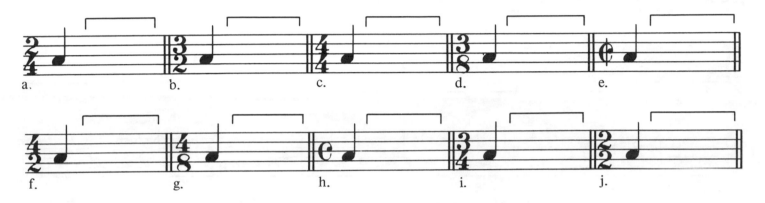

3. Complete the following bars with rests.

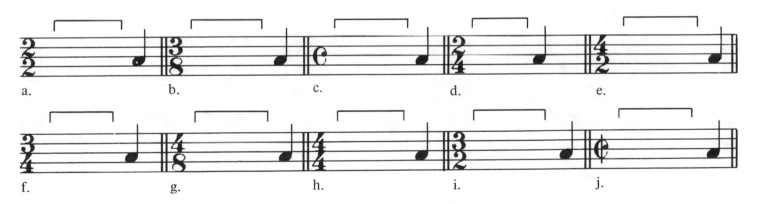

4. Complete the following bars with rests.

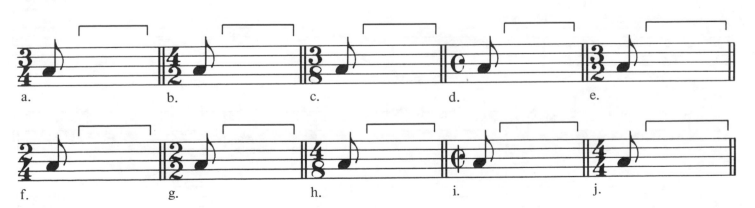

5. Complete the following bars with rests.

a.　　　　　　b.　　　　　　c.　　　　　　d.　　　　　　e.

f.　　　　　　g.　　　　　　h.　　　　　　i.　　　　　　j.

184

6. Rewrite the following bars, grouping the notes into beats.

example:

185

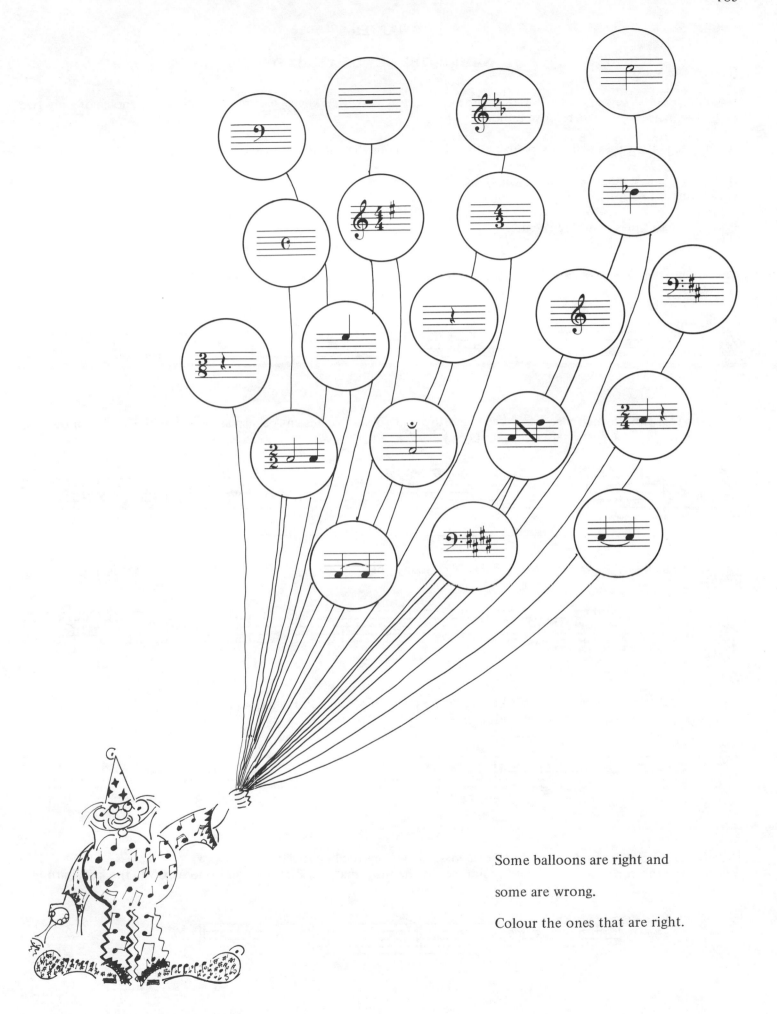

Some balloons are right and

some are wrong.

Colour the ones that are right.

CHAPTER 8

NAMING THE KEY OF A MELODY

If you are asked to name the key of a tune that is written with a key signature you will have a choice of only two keys: the major key or its relative minor.

At this stage the tunes will only be using the major scale or the harmonic form of the minor scale.

If the tune is in a major key there will be no added accidentals.
If the tune is in a minor key the leading note (if used) will be raised.

Look at these tunes and play them.

This tune has a key signature of two sharps. It contains only the notes of the scale of D major, so it is in the key of D major.

However this tune, which also has a key signature of two sharps, has an A sharp as an accidental so it is in the key of B minor. (The A♯ is the raised leading note.)

This tune has a key signature of two flats. It contains only the notes of the scale of B♭ major so it is in the key of B♭ major.

However this tune, which also has a key signature of two flats, has an F sharp as an accidental so it is in the key of G minor. (The F sharp is the raised leading note.)

Here is a short cut for finding the name of a major key from the key signature.
Sharp keys: the tonic of every sharp major key is the note that is a diatonic semitone ABOVE the last sharp in the key signature.

Flat keys: the tonic of every flat key is the same as the next-to-the-last flat in the key signature.

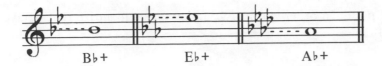

Note: For F major you will just have to remember that it has one flat.

Exercises

Name the key of each of these melodies.

key _____

key _____

key _____

key _____

key _____

key _____

key _____

key _____

key _____

key _____

TRANSPOSITION

TRANSPOSITION means a change of pitch. In other words if you play music in a different octave or in a different key than it is written you are transposing it.

TRANSPOSITION UP AN OCTAVE means that you must rewrite the melody so that each note sounds one octave higher than in the original. Sometimes you will use the same clef and sometimes you may change clef.

TRANSPOSITION DOWN AN OCTAVE means that every note must sound an octave lower than in the original.

EXERCISES

1. Transpose these notes up an octave in the treble clef.

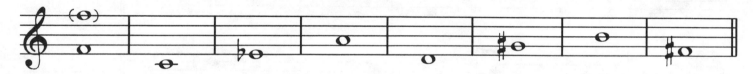

2. Transpose these notes down an octave in the treble clef.

3. Transpose these notes up an octave in the bass clef.

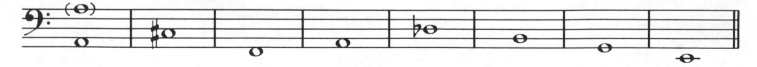

4. Transpose these notes down an octave in the bass clef.

5. Transpose these notes down an octave using the bass clef.

6. Transpose these notes up an octave using the treble clef.

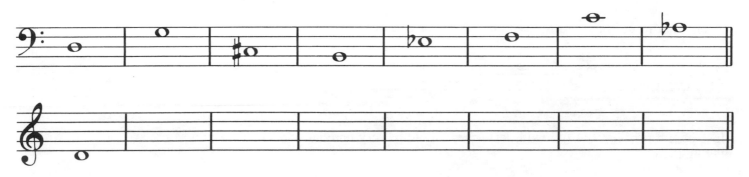

This is the beginning of London Bridge Is Falling Down.

This is what it looks like transposed up an octave using the treble clef.

This is what it looks like transposed down an octave using the bass clef.

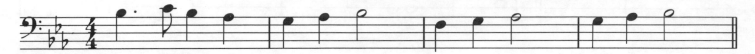

Most of the tunes in the following exercises should be very familiar to you. See if you can recognize them without playing them.

EXERCISES

1. Transpose the following down an octave using the treble clef.

2. Transpose the following up an octave using the treble clef.

3. Transpose the following down one octave using the bass clef.

4. Transpose the following up one octave using the bass clef.

5. Transpose the following down one octave using the bass clef.

6. Transpose the following up one octave using the treble clef.

ACROSS

4.  is ——— time.

6. is a ——— semitone.

9. Use your foot for this.
10. The next two notes up from D.
12. There are high notes and ——— notes.
13. Musical term for 'with'
14.
15. The note you raise in a minor scale.
17. There are usually ——— pedals on a piano.
18. The key of A minor has ——— sharps.
21. Playfully.
22. is a ——— third.
24. 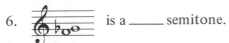 is ——— time.
27. 'medium'
28. Abbreviation for medium soft.
29. A piece for two players.
31. 'right hand'
32. The hammer hits the ———.
33. 'una'
35. D major has ——— sharps.
38. An accidental.
40.  These notes move ———.
41. Italian word for 'not'.

DOWN

1. is a half ———.
2.
3. Adagio.
5. As soft as possible.
6. Sweetly.
7. The note below B.
8. The first one is usually accented.
11. The dominant is ——— notes up.
12. Slowly.
14. Time.
15. Sudden accent.
16.
19. D is the ——— of this triad.
20. Every quarter note has one.
21. Gracefully.
22. Less.
23. Rapidly.
25. Gradually getting slower.
26. Soft.
30. A chord with 3 notes built up in thirds.
34. 'fine'.
35. Abbreviation for 'hold'.
36. Measure.
37. D minor has ——— flat.
39. These notes move ———.

198

TEST PAPER #1

10   I   Write the following notes as quarter notes.

Bb   E   G   F#   A   C   Db   B   G#   F

10   II   Write these scales in the treble clef ascending and descending using the correct key signature for each. Mark each semitone with a slur.

A major in half notes.

D minor melodic in whole notes.

10   III   Write this tune an octave higher in the treble clef.

8   IV   Beside each note write the note that is a chromatic semitone higher.

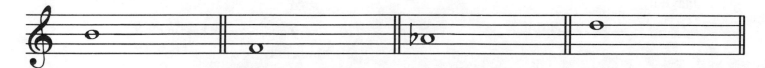

8   V   Beside each note write the note that is a diatonic semitone lower.

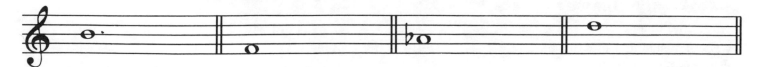

10   VI   Complete these bars with rests.

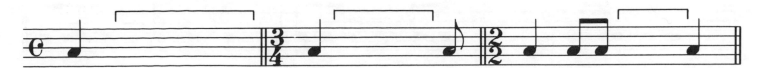

6   VII   Name the key of each of these melodies.

key: —————

key: —————

10   VIII   Name each of these intervals.

—————   —————   —————   —————   —————

8   IX   Explain these musical terms.

Allegro ————————————————————

rit.   ————————————————————

vivace ————————————————————

staccato ————————————————————

8   X   Write these triads using the correct key signature for each.

     a.   the tonic triad of E major.
     b.   the dominant triad of F minor.
     c.   the dominant triad of A flat major.
     d.   the tonic triad of B minor.

        a.   b.   c.   d.

6   XI   Give the correct time signature for each of these bars

6   XII   Name the major and the minor key for each of these key signatures.

major key: _____ _____ _____

minor key: _____ _____ _____

TEST PAPER #2

10   I   Write these scales in the bass clef ascending and descending using accidentals instead of a key signature for each one. Label the dominant notes.

B flat major in half notes.

C minor harmonic in quarter notes.

10   II   Beside each note write the note that is a whole tone lower.

6   III   Name the key of each of these melodies.

key: _____

key: _____

10   IV   Name these notes.

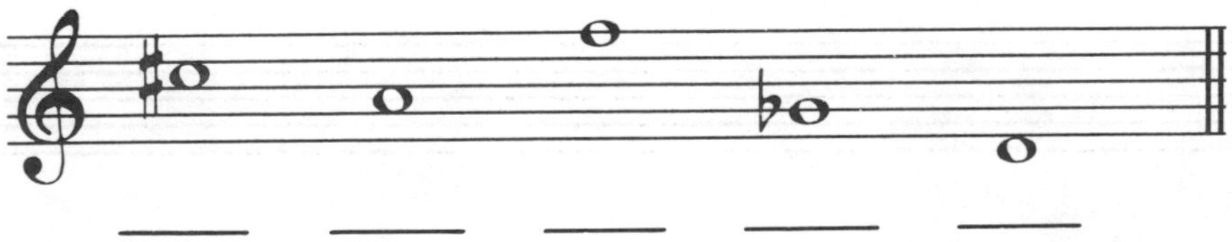

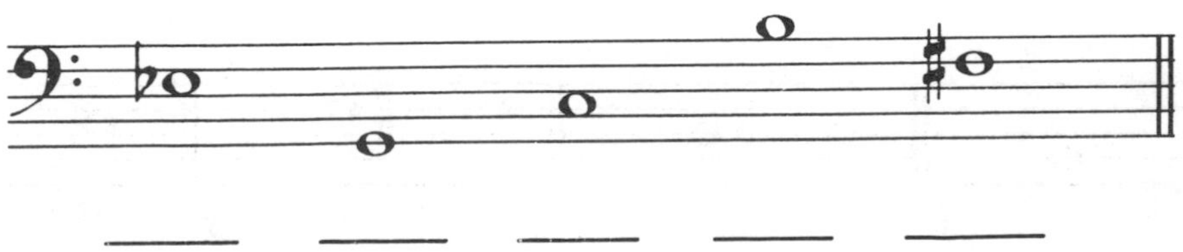

6   V   Explain these musical terms.

           crescendo _____

           andante _____

           giocoso _____

6   VI   Write these triads using accidentals instead of key signatures.
                a.   tonic triad of D major.
                b.   Dominant triad of G minor.
                c.   tonic triad of F sharp minor.

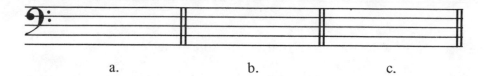

10   VII   Write this tune an octave lower in the bass clef.

10   VIII   State whether each of these is a chromatic semitone (c.s.) or a diatonic semitone (d.s.)

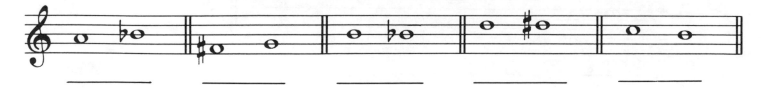

10 IX Complete these bars with rests.

8 X Write these as melodic intervals.

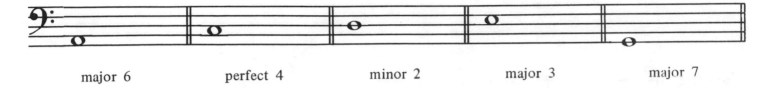

major 6   perfect 4   minor 2   major 3   major 7

6 XI Write the correct key signature for each of these keys.

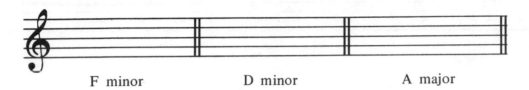

F minor   D minor   A major

8 XII Give the correct time signature for each of these bars

TEST PAPER #3

10   I   Write this tune an octave higher in the treble clef.

10   II   Complete these bars with rests.

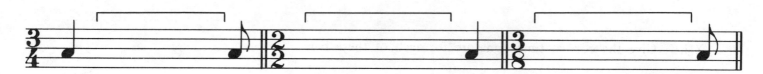

10   III   Name these notes.

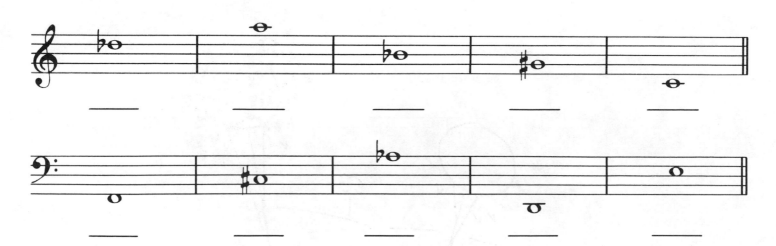

10   IV   Write these scales ascending and descending using the correct key signature for each.
              a.   G minor harmonic in whole notes.
              b.   E major in quarter notes.

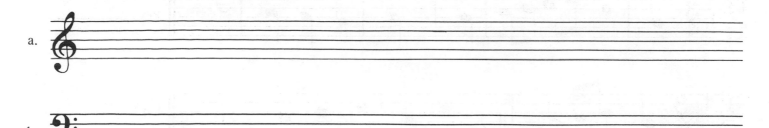

8   V   Put the correct time signature at the beginning of each bar.

8   VI   Write these triads using the correct key signature for each.

              a.   the dominant triad of C minor.
              b.   the tonic triad of A major.
              c.   the tonic triad of E minor.
              d.   the dominant triad of B flat major.

10   VII   Beside each note write the note that is a diatonic semitone higher.

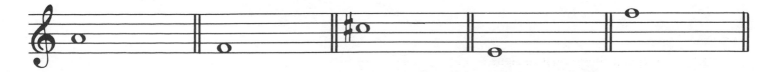

6   VIII   Name the key of each of these melodies.

key: _____

key: _____

key: _____

10   IX   Write the correct key signature for each of these keys.

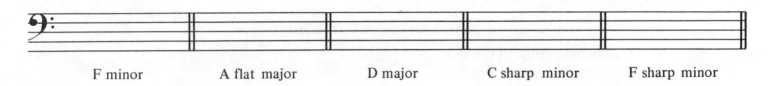

    F minor   A flat major   D major   C sharp minor   F sharp minor

10   X   Write these intervals

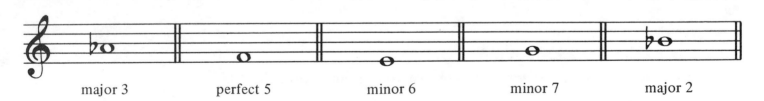

    major 3   perfect 5   minor 6   minor 7   major 2

8   XI   Explain these musical signs.

𝄐   _____

pp   _____

sfz   _____

    _____

INDEX